"The greatest service that can be rendered to any country

is the introduction of a useful plant."

Thomas Jefferson

Third President of the
United States of America

ISBN 1-900489-08-2

9 781900 489089 >

Published by Mr A.K. SMITH

Printed by SUNPRINT 38 Tay Street, Perth PH1 5TT

Front Cover: Portrait of David Douglas
Courtesy of The Linean Society
All photographs and Maps © A.K. SMITH

CONTENTS

PREFACE

"That's Douglas Fir", the foreman made this statement with considerable emphasis on the word Douglas. He did not extend this gem of botanical knowledge further. I acknowledged the fact without comment. Snedding, wielding an axe to debranch fallen trees, was hard work for a schoolboy. This holiday work was a prelude to final study and then the inevitable National Service in Her Majesty's forces. Forestry did not figure in the future, short or long term.

Over two years later, on that same site, I was planting a second crop of Douglas Fir, resin gets into the blood very easily. From a barrack room in Berlin, I wrote to find out about forestry as a career. Most of my contemporaries commenced by planting small trees on bare hillsides in a land of little forest. Fate and the fifty-three storm which felled many a mature wood, gave me a perspective of the potential of those exotic trees.

Knowledge came at Forestry School. A David Douglas had introduced the fir which bore his name. There were others of equal merit which he had introduced to this country, but none so definitively attributed to him. Botanical texts told of whence came those sylvan treasures and where in this country they excelled. Marks were gained in examinations by mentioning origins such as Oregon and sites such as Scone, both unseen. Theory was ever thus, the instructors passing facts to the instructed. Practical problems to overcome, good practice for the future, was the core of the course.

A posting to Perthshire opened new horizons. Early in the sixties, I visited Scone. That venerable body, the Royal Scottish Forestry Society, was allowed the privilege of holding its Annual General Meeting in the purlieus of the Palace. A tour of the Arboretum was led by Lord Mansfield. He started at a favoured Douglas Fir and told of a tree grown from seed sent home in 1826 from the Columbia River of Western North America, by David Douglas. It was a memorable occasion and when, years later, the grounds were opened to the public, I used a day's holiday, specially taken, to visit that tree again. Over many years later, junior colleagues and friends from North America, were brought to view it, and its fellows.

The fair City of Perth holds much of value to the history and heritage of its shire. By the late sixties, I had found my way to the Local Studies Department of the Sandeman Library. The firm but ever helpful Miss Essler guarded its treasures. Most appropriately, there I met David Douglas in his Journal. Reading it was inspirational. This wonderful work was first published during 1914.

As my empathy grew with David Douglas over decades, he became David a fellow in forestry in this wonderful sylvan county of Perthshire. Bachelors both we seemed united over time. To visit the land he travelled and see the ancient woods he walked through, became a dream long unrealised. A friend, an American of Scottish descent, spent time bringing me a taste of the treasure. Her reports on tape of the wonders of the temperate rain forest, served only to whet my appetite.

At last in 1989, I flew to Vancouver and had the holiday of a lifetime. On that and other occasions, this lady chauffeured me over thousands of miles from California to British Columbia. Most importantly, she consented to become my wife and come to live in the land of her forebears, six short years ago.

Archie Smith
1997

CHRONOLOGY

of

Improvement in Scotland and Exploration of Ecotopia

during the lives of

Archibald Menzies, David Douglas, John Jeffrey

1754	-	Archibald Menzies born at Styx near Aberfeldy, Perthshire.
	-	The Scots Gardeners Director by James Justice published.
1755	-	The Edinburgh Society for Encouraging Arts, Science, Manufactures, and Agriculture founded.
1755	-	Kew Gardens founded under Lord Bute with William Aiton as first Superintendent.
1765	-	Scottish Society for the Importation of Foreign Seeds founded.
1766	-	Nursery founded on Scone Estate.
1767	-	Nursery founded on the lower slope of Kinnoul Hill, Perth.
1768	-	Seed sent from Quebec to Scotland.
1772	-	Kew sends out first scientific traveller, Francis Masson.
1774	-	Extensive afforestation commenced by 4th Duke of Atholl.
1775	-	Treatise on Forest Trees by William Boucher, published.
1777	-	Flora Scotica by Lightfoot published.
1783	-	Highland and Agricultural Society (for improvement) founded.
	-	North West Fur Company founded in Montreal by Scots.
1792	-	A Menzies sails up the Columbia River on the Naval Survey.
1799	-	David Douglas born in Scone Parish, Perthshire.
1804	-	Horticultural Societies founded at Perth and London.
	-	John C. Loudon plans Scone policy for the Earl of Mansfield.
1811	-	David Douglas has started his career in Scone Estate Gardens.
	-	Scots, recruited from North West Company, found Fort Astoria.
	-	First North West party reaches it at the Columbia mouth.
1812	-	Astoria taken by Northwesters and retained as Fort George.
1820	-	David Douglas moves to Glasgow Botanic Gardens.
1821	-	North West Company amalgamates with Hudson Bay Company.
1823	-	David Douglas travels to New York and around, on behalf of the Horticultural Society of London.
	-	James Fennimore Cooper publishes his first Leatherstocking novel based on the early British pioneers in that area.

1825	-	In a similar historical situation, Fort George at the mouth of the Columbia River is re-sited inland as Fort Vancouver.
	-	David Douglas, arriving by sea, reaches the uncompleted Fort.
1827	-	After two years, Douglas crosses the Rocky Mountains to Hudson Bay and return to the U.K.
1830	-	Back to the Columbia River again, then to California.
1832	-	Returns to the Columbia.
1833	-	Douglas travels north to New Caledonia and returns to the Columbia. He leaves for Honolulu before the year ends.
1834	-	David Douglas dies on Hawaii as a result of an accident.
1850	-	The Oregon Botanical Association of Scotland founded to import seed from Western North America (Ecotopia).
	-	John Jeffrey of the Edinburgh Botanic Garden Staff sails to Hudson Bay, travels over the Rockies.

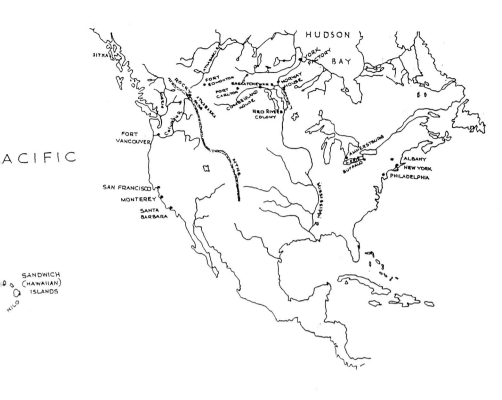

The principal places associated with David Douglas in North America

CHAPTER ONE

Scone and Scotland

"Let us now praise illustrious men,
our ancestors in their successive generations"

So intoned the Minister of Scone Old Parish Church in Perthshire. His audience stood in the churchyard on a damp, dull October afternoon of 1988. They were gathered to honour the memory of a local man, David Douglas, born one hundred and eighty-nine years before.

The minister stood before a substantial stone monument erected to his memory, which had dominated the churchyard for well over a century. Time and the climate had blurred the message carried on its panels, the destiny of many others. However, Scone could not forget this favoured son. Despite the demands on community and Kirk, the parishioners started a special fund to refurbish this monument. Now they met in a service of rededication.

The minister's reading from the Book of Ecclesiasticus continued with those words -

"Some left a name behind them, so their praises are still sung.
While others have left no memory, and disappeared as though they had not existed".

This little group of local people who silently endured the increasing dampness, testified that David Douglas was not forgotten at his roots.

The Minister of Scone's second reading was particularly appropriate -

"When through the woods and forest glades I wander
and hear the birds sing sweetly in the trees,
and I look down from lofty mountain grandeur
and hear the brook and feel the gentle breeze.
How great thou art.".

David Douglas loved nature and never ceased to honour one whom he believed to have been its Creator.

A local lady unveiled a plaque to mark the event. The ceremony completed, a very welcome repast refreshed the patient participants on this dreich day. Warm and dry again, they might have gone home then. Perthshire parishes have their local heroes abundantly. Most are legends in their own land, but Douglas was different.

A talk and slide show completed this memorable day. Within the walls of the homely church hall, an audience followed a trail west to another hemisphere. They saw a land of mountain grandeur, great rivers, and giant trees, ferns and flowers. The speaker had travelled thousands of miles to enhance their day and reward their labours.

Chance had brought the President of the David Douglas Society of Western North America to Scotland and Scone that year. An eminent Forest Officer, recently retired, on a pilgrimage to the home of their hero, his visit was fortuitous. The Society's members reside along the Pacific Coast of North America from California to Alaska. They meet at a different venue each year. Pipers play before a banquet where toasts are drunk to the memory of David Douglas. Learned lecturers give orations in his honour. This is a select Society, but the spirit is akin to the many who honour Scotland's national bard across the world.

The paradox of David Douglas is that it is his native land and the continent of Europe which should honour him. He sought the botanical treasures of North America. They have enriched his country and continent beyond measure. From house gardens to great forests, the heritage of Douglas is present. Few people have brought such pleasure and profit to succeeding generations in such a viable form.

Few have had such a short, interesting life in this field. Few have received such a limited recognition by writers of biography. If semi-fictional work is excepted, only his own journals and a later edited selective version of part of them, have been published in the United Kingdom. To British Columbia goes the honour of a worthy memoir written fifty years ago. Douglas of the Fir, by Athelstan George Harvey.

The subject of this North American study is believed to have been born on the 25th of June 1799. At the end of a century which had transformed his native land. It was now a dynamic partner in an expanding empire. From around 1740 a remarkable intellectual development had occurred.

"Scottish Enlightenment was the natural, almost the inevitable, outcome of several centuries of Scottish and European intellectual history". This general statement applies to many disciplines, not least natural science. Improvement of the understanding of the natural world was one facet. Foremost was the improvement of man's understanding of himself and improvement of his state. Enlightenment begat Improvement, the land was valued as never before. Lord Kames, the Laird of Blairdrummond, was one who combined legal, philosophical, and literary inquiry with agricultural application. His book, The Gentleman Farmer, being an attempt to improve Agriculture, by subjecting it to the Test of Rational Principles, published in 1766, was indicative of the era.

David Douglas's birthplace is believed to have been the ancient settlement of Scone, perhaps the medieval burgh itself. This sacred site saw the development of Church and Crown over countless centuries. Celtic and later kings were crowned by clergy, Celtic and Catholic. After the Reformation, its glory faded, Abbey, Palace, and lands passed to a line of lairds, the Murray Lords Stormont. Men of achievement in the wider national field, they became Lords Mansfield of the United Kingdom peerage. In time they planned a new palace with pleasure grounds around.

Three years before David Douglas's birth, the Minister of Scone Parish describes the site -

"Round the house, except on the south west, where it is open runs a shrubbery and young plantation, intersected with serpentine gravel walks; and mixed with old trees, among the largest and finest in the country". The new palace was commenced as the new century began and the greater landscaped area planned. John Claudius Loudon, the genius of his time, was the architect. 1804 also saw the publication of his book, Observations on the Formation and Management of Useful and Ornamental Plantations; on the Theory and Practice of Landscape-Gardening, and on embarking Land from Rivers or the Sea.

Three other events were to take place that year relevant to the life and career of David Douglas. In nearby Perth and far off London, Horticultural Societies were inaugurated. Both would in time add Royal to their title. Locally the parish church, stone by stone, started a journey of about two miles to a new site.

On the 9th of May 1805, the relocated kirk opened for worship. Planned new villages were part of this Enlightenment driven Age of Improvement. Of Old Scone only the cemetery and the medieval burgh cross remain. The grounds of the Palace could now be extended and a great arboretum planned.

It is believed that David Douglas began the long journey of his short life by moving to New Scone. He was nearer the Fair City of Perth and in time walked to school. His route was across Kinnoul Hill to a destination on the east bank of the Tay. Now gifted to the city, this eminence then, as now, was wooded. Even the lower slopes would be wilder than at present. Like William Wordsworth's growing boy, Nature was all in all to young David, the nursery of his formative years.

At age eleven, he entered another nursery which would enhance his education further. Now it was back to Old Scone and the privilege of becoming an apprentice gardener in the Earl of Mansfield's employ. Here he was to meet the plants of the explored temperate world. Plant science was dynamic in the age of improvement. Head Gardener Beattie was described as one of the best of his profession. He and his subordinate McGillivray early recognised Douglas's potential and invested in his future.

Scottish gardening was a noble profession. The great estates were engaged in a competition of excellence. The United Kingdom overall benefited from its products. Gardeners who could make exotic plants bloom in the less kindly climate of the northern kingdom, were in demand south of the border.

Medicine and horticulture were related sciences. As early as 1670, Doctors Balfour and Sibbold leased a piece of land in Edinburgh for a Physic Garden. After many moves the ongoing project became the Royal Botanic Garden at its present site since 1823. The Chelsea Physic Garden in London followed in 1673. Nurseries were founded, trade catalogues and books published as the eighteenth century progressed. The Prince and Princess of Wales had their grounds at Kew landscaped. Their friend the third Earl of Bute, a keen botanist, carried on the work. He was the first effective Director of the famous Kew Garden. In 1759, the Princess appointed William Aiton as first Curator. He and his son were a worthy dynasty

The eighteenth century was dynamic in the creation of woods as well as gardens. Silviculture and horticulture were synonymous. The expansion required new plant material from overseas. In Edinburgh during 1765, a Society for the Importation of Foreign Seeds was founded under the chair of the eminent Professor of Botany at Edinburgh University, John Hope. Imports were made from Carolina, Philadelphia, and Quebec. Francis Masson from Aberdeen was the first "scientific traveller" to use Sir Joseph Bank's title, sent out from Kew during 1772.

David Douglas, under the tutelage of Mr. Beattie and his own dynamic, might have become as celebrated a gardening professional as the Aitons. Perhaps it was Mr. Beattie's introducing him to the Brown brothers which ensured that he too would become a scientific traveller, the greatest of all. The Browns had one of the Perth Nurseries with its wealth of foreign species, but they also were interested in the flora of their native land. Did their enthusiasm for expedition to the Highlands open new windows of opportunity?

Seven years at Scone ended his formal apprenticeship. Education was valued in Scotland. David spent the winter of 1817-8 attending a private school at Perth. With Mr. Beattie's highest recommendation, David Douglas now obtained a prime private estate post at Valleyfield in Fife. The venue may have lacked the grandeur of Scone, but there was another great attraction. The gardens contained the greatest collection of exotic plants held in private possession. David was assistant to another worthy mentor, the Curator Alexander Stewart. The learned laird, Sir Alexander Preston, was known for the riches of his botanical library, a treasure correctly guarded. David was given the rare privilege of access.

After Valleyfield only one further career move was possible; employment at one of the University-managed Botanic Gardens of Edinburgh or Glasgow. Both were under most eminent Professors, men of the wide world of Botany. Hope in

Edinburgh was the friend of Sir Joseph Banks, Director of Kew. He corresponded with the celebrated Count Carol Linneas, the famous father of botanical classification. Another Perthshire gardener, Archibald Menzies, had found his friendship and eventually became both a Botanist and Doctor of Medicine. He too was sent from Kew as a scientific traveller by Sir Joseph Banks.

David Douglas went to Glasgow Botanic Garden as subordinate to its Curator, Stewart Murray. Once again he had an inspiring immediate superior willing to nurture his genius to the full. David attended the early morning lectures given by the Professor of Botany to mainly medical students. They were the brilliant products of a brilliant mind. William Jackson Hooker was also relatively new to Glasgow. His personality was kindly, as warm as his exuberant enthusiasm for his subject. Drawn from different backgrounds, botany was the catalyst which made those two young men enduring friends.

If contact with the Brown brothers of Perth had whetted David Douglas's appetite to become an ecological explorer and plant detective, fate favoured that ambition. Hooker had a project, to produce a definitive Flora Scotica. John Lightfoot, the travelling companion of Thomas Pennant had published a work of that name in 1777. A protege of Professor Hope, James Robertson, travelled the Highlands on behalf of the Commissioners of the Annexed Estates shortly before. The new work required a much more extensive survey, especially over the less accessible areas.

Hooker and Douglas tramped over the Highlands and Islands together. They must have carried many a burden over weary miles, sleeping rough, and enjoying the achievements of the day. Of David, Hooker was to later write that "his great activity, undaunted courage, a singular abstemiousness and energetic zeal, at once pointed him out as an individual eminently calculated to do himself credit as a scientific traveller."

From Masson onwards, Scots were pre-eminent in this field. When the Horticultural Society of London required to recruit another, they wrote to Professor Hooker at Glasgow. David Douglas was the perfect person, a professional who would be able to achieve the best results his situation in that country permitted.

When David left for London that spring of 1823, he left in Glasgow, friends. He had become attached to Hooker's sons, when a guest in his home. Like his father, the eldest was to become his correspondent.

China had been the intended destination of the new traveller, but diplomatic problems intervened. The substitute was to be U.S.A., New York State and its surrounds. It was but a prelude to a greater project on that continent.

CHAPTER TWO

Gateway to The New World

"This being my birthday (I completed my twenty fourth year) and the market day of my native place, I could not help thinking over the days that were gone". So wrote David Douglas in his journal on the 25th June 1823. He was homesick for the lovely land left behind, old Scone, old Scotland, thousands of years of settlement and tradition. It is said that all who leave Scotland carry a part of this little land in their heart. David was to be no exception. His wonderful journals tell of his travels and portray himself.

London was left on the 3rd, Liverpool on the 6th, progress was poor on almost windless seas. When at last the Azores were sighted, the wind rose and the Captain decided to sail on to recover lost time.

Deeply disappointed, David as usual immersed himself in study. Spanish grammar was a great relief from the tedium. The Transactions of the Linnean Society completed his intellectual fare. Essentially an energetic explorer on land, this waste of seas wearied him.

"This morning can never be effaced; it had rained a little during the night, which cooled the atmosphere and added a hue to Nature's work, which was truly grand - the fine orchards of Long Island on the one side, and the variety of soil and vegetation of Staten on the other. I once more thought myself happy". David Douglas landed on the New York of his time, the 6th of August 1823.

Forty years after their foundation, the United States of America had moved mightily. Their Third President, Thomas Jefferson, with imagination and courage initiated the purchase of the Louisiana territory from an improvident Napoleon Bonaparte. The official western frontier became the Rocky Mountain summits. President Munro's Doctrine inferred that the Pacific might yet be the prize. David Douglas came to a young nation with a vigorous outgoing people. The ideals of the Scottish Enlightenment had played a significant role in the birth of the new nation. Jefferson, Madison, and Munro all had Scottish mentors. Williamsburgh, Philadelphia, and Princeton had Colleges cum Universities with distinguished Scottish Principals. One Dr. Witherspoon, had contributed much to the sentiments of and was a signatory to, the Declaration of Independence.

As with other sciences, botany advanced. André Micheau after exploration had produced his Flora Boreali-Americana, published during the year of the Lousiana Purchase. The following one, President Jefferson dispatched the famed Corp of Discovery led by Captains Lewis and Clark. They traversed the new Territory, crossed the Continental Divide, and paddled to the Pacific. They lacked a David Douglas, but plants were collected and brought back. To Frederick Pursh, an Austrian, was given the task of classification. There is a suggestion that the best specimens went home with him, but Flora America Septronalis was published in

1817. That year also saw the first botanical book in English, Thomas Nuttal's Genera of North American Plants. David Douglas arrived proficient in all three, quoting them in his journal.

Today, New York is the spectacular nerve centre of the nation, not only a national but an international leader of industry and commerce. David Douglas arrived before the boom commenced. Settlement of the New Netherlands preceded him by two hundred years. It began up the Hudson River at Fort Orange (Albany) and later New Amsterdam (New York). Between rose extensive estates. The landowners, the patroons, bore names such as Van Renssalaer, Van Cortlandt, Roosevelt.

Fruit flourished in this land, introduced by the Dutch and improved in a kindly climate, since the days of the legendary governor, Peter Stuvesand. David's principle remit was the procurement of fruit trees at prudent prices. However, he was also to botanise when possible. The whole would prove a test of his knowledge, character, and overall professionalism.

The Horticultural Society had corresponding members of considerable social standing in the State. His first visit was to two of the most distinguished, Doctors Torrey and Hosack. Dr. John Torrey, Physician and botanist, was the more prominent. Douglas mentions him only once. "I called on Dr. Torrey whom I found an intelligent botanist, an agreeable person, and much disposed to aid me". This may have been an over kindly appreciation of an arrogant individual.

Dr. David Hosack was different. David's entry on meeting with his first American came on his first day on shore. He "began to feel uneasy after having such a long passage, and then to be perplexed". Then he "had an interview with Dr. Hosack; the cordial manner in which I was received by this gentleman made an impression upon me". This understatement would be upgraded many times in the future. On Hosack's recommendation, a Mr. Hogg, a recent immigrant in business as a nurseryman and florist, showed David round the city.

Next on the agenda was a visit to another corresponding member of the Society. Mr. Prince had a nursery at Flushing. He had an extensive catalogue which did not come up to expectation, when Douglas visited his over weedy ground. Prince was to be a problem in the future.

Across the Hudson were the finest fruit farms. One old Dutch farmer had 24 interesting varieties of peaches on his 20 acre allotment. Plums were also plentiful. Thanks to Dr. Hosack, a very fine one was found. David's entry in his journal of the 15th August indicates how far he had travelled in happiness over ten days. "Thanks to the medium of Dr. Hosack I learned of a fine plum named 'Washington', a name which every product in the United States that is great or good is called".

Hosack and Hogg were his guardian angels. He dined with the Doctor after divine service and spent the evening at his house. Next, accompanied by Hogg, he set off for New Jersey and William Penn's city of brotherly love. Rich, well cultivated land on the road to Trenton appeared an eternal garden. The celebrated Coxe (of apple fame) repaid a visit with promise of fruit to come.

Philadelphia, a garden city did not disappoint. Benjamin Franklin, its greatest citizen had planted in Perthshire - Scots Pine trees on Blairdrummond Estate. He had been a friend of its improver laird, Lord Kames. Kindness cascaded on the young Scot. Treasures were promised if he returned at a more appropriate time.

On the return journey to New York, the erstwhile gardener from Scone spent a night in Perth Amboy. Built on a point of the latter name, it owed its origin to the 4th Earl of Perth. One book which must have been required reading at Scone would have been The Scots Gardener. This first book on the subject was published first in 1683. Two years later, John Reid, its author, surveyed the estates of his employer in New Jersey. This included the little town on the banks of the Rariton River.

The tongue of good report had been heard on the Society's scientific traveller. On the 1st of September he "attended in the evening a committee meeting of the New York Horticultural Society, for the purpose of offering their assistance to me during my residence in this city. Mr. Hoffman, Esq., the President, is a man of reputation, being a wealthy merchant here. He uses me with all possible attention imaginable; invited me to stay at his house all night, which I did".

Three days later, David Douglas sailed up the Hudson River on the most important part of his mission. On an infinitely grander scale it resembled a journey up the valley of his native Tay. Great estates surrounded the river where the land was most fertile. Like north of the Highland Line, sparser settlement was on a poorer land won from broad-leaved forest.

"The scenery was particularly fine on the west side; the perpendicular rocks covered with wood gave it an appearance seldom to be met with. About forty miles from New York, in the highlands, many pleasant villas are seen from the river. West point is still pointed out to strangers, being the place where the unfortunate, but good, Major Andre paid the debt of nature in his country's defence. The approach to the Fort and Military School on the north has a beautiful effect".

Eighty miles up river was the seat of General Morgan Lewis, a former state governor. The great man was from home, but the son of an immediate neighbour deputised in his stead. James Thomson Jnr. of Ellerslie took David from the

Tavern to his house. The surrounds were in cultivation, four large oaks of different species remained, acorns were promised.

Next it was on to Albany, the former Fort Orange of the Dutch. As King Charles II had favoured his brother, the Duke of York with his acquisition to the Empire, New Amsterdam became New York. Albany, the Duke's Scottish title, was conferred on this town.

Here was the state capital and the current governor, De Witt Clinton. David sought his advice on furthering his project. "I waited on His Excellency the Governor, who said that his opinion was for me to proceed to Canada without delay, the season being far advanced, and particularly as the steamboat Superior was to sail from Buffalo next".

Following this gubernatorial advice, David Douglas journeyed on over increasingly rougher roads. He changed for a part to the new Erie Canal, almost complete. The forest still flourished intriguing the future Douglas of the Fir. "Passed some large swamps of fir, walnut, ash, oak, elm. I here, to my astonishment, found a magnolia ten feet high, leaves large, smooth, ovate, and acute. I saw no more but itself; no seed on it; had no appearance of having flowered. David's journal increases in quantity and quality the further he travels from New York. In Scottish terms, he had crossed the Highland Line. Another day on saw him breakfasting "at Caledonia, a settlement of Scotch people. Country generally flat; by roadside stands settlements in infancy, just clearing the grounds by burning".

On the 16th September, David Douglas crossed to Canada. He sailed west along Lake Erie from Buffalo to Amhertsburg a garrison town of Upper Canada Ontario. His host was a Mr. Brisco, who immediately with gun and dogs, introduced him to the woods.

"This is what I might term my first day in America". There is no mistaking the sheer joy and exuberance in this statement.

"The trees in the woods were of astonishing magnitude. The soil, in general, over which we passed was a rich black earth, and seemed to be formed of decomposed vegetables".

At last David Douglas had reached the "forest primeval" beloved of Longfellow.

"I made a visit to a small island in the River Detroit opposite to Amherstburg. It is about one mile long and three quarters at its greatest breadth; it appeared to be a spot worthy of notice, as I found before evening. The whole island is low, and soil is very rich black loam covered with trees of large seize. Quercus sp 44 Herb., trees from 50 to 70 feet high, 40 feet without branches. With a shot from my gun I cut some branches, leaves and acorns. They seem to be to be fine, and different from any which I had seen before. With a few shots more I secured specimens and paper of seeds".

Ten times more is written on that day's expedition to the little island. David's journal was now totally changed. The almost mandatory entries for the consumption of his employers have been replaced by his personal and professional appreciation of the environment it was his privilege to explore. Now appears the botanist of the exploring expeditions with Professor Hooker, north of the Highland Line.

Day after day, David records the plethora of plants to be found over this fertile forest, a treasury of trees with pearls within. The humblest excites and enthuses the ecologist. In a long swamp intersected by natural ditches, he finds "Eriocaulon, a small species and much like our British one on Loch Sligachan, Sky".

Journal entries constantly include, "Quercus sp.. Herb." and a number. Oaks were a key constituent of the herbaruim of one who must have walked among the western woods of his native land. Not for nothing had he read Pursh, often quoted. He produced "some Account of the American Oaks, particularly of such species as were met with during a Journey...............in the Year 1823 by David Douglas". He writes in this document; "The oaks, from their number and beauty and the acknowledged utility of their wood, particularly attracted my attention, and of the thirty four species enumerated by Pursh as natives of the vast continent of North America, I was fortunate to meet with no less than nineteen".

This interesting dissertation commences with White Oak, Quercus Alba. "It is one of the largest, most abundant, and useful species in the middle states, found upon every variety of soil. Towards the middle and Western extremity of the State of New York in the Genessee Tract, where the soil is generally a dry rich black or brownish loam, it attains an immense size. On the banks of the River Detroit from Amherstburg to the junction of the Thames with the St. Clair in Upper Canada, and on the opposite banks, in the Michigan Territory, on a deep alluvial rich black soil, those trees frequently measure from 20 to 25 feet in circumference at 8 feet from the ground, and are from 80 to 100 feet high." David had knowledge to add to that of his predecessors.

The most detailed oak in the Account is the last, obviously added years later. Though previously seen from the sea Douglas found Quercus garryana inland on the west side of the continent. He had "great pleasure in dedicating this species to M. Garry, Esq., Deputy Governor of the Hudson Bay company, as a simple token of regard". Far beyond the ken of Pursh and Michaux, it appeared in Professor Hooker's Flora Boreali-Americana. That, however, was a continent away from his travels of 1823.

Scientific traveller was the designation of David Douglas at this time. In the future, scientific adventurer would become another very appropriate description of a brave man. The wiles of Native Americans often provided problems. Surprisingly, it was an African American who introduced him to the unexpected in human contacts. This gentleman was one of the many slaves who fled north to freedom above the 49th Parallel.

Alone except for this driver of a horse-drawn vehicle, David was well away from the settlement of Sandwich by Lake Saint Clair. Inevitably it was an oak, number 43 of his herbarium, which was the locus.

"I got up in the oak 43 for the purpose of procuring seeds and specimens; the day being warm, I was induced to take off my coat and in that state I ascended. I had not been five minutes up, when to my surprise the man whom I hired as guide and assistant took up my coat and made off as fast as he could run with it. I descended almost headlong and followed, but before I could get near him he escaped in the wood......I was thus left five miles from where I had left the car, in a miserable condition, and as there was no remedy that could be taken to better myself, I tied my seeds in my neckcloth and made to my lodging."

One other problem presented itself in this multi-ethnic society. "I had to hire a man to take me back to Sandwich as I could not drive; the horse only understood the French language, and I could not talk to him in his tongue, placed me in an awkward situation".

Though trivial when set against the almost fatal incidents in future years, this one effectively ended his outreach in Canada.

"The loss of my coat and money, bad weather - all combined made me glad to relinquish the idea of Canada at such a late period of the season. It certainly is a fine field and would afford an abundant harvest".

September ending, it was back to Buffalo on the road home. Niagara was near and worthy of a visit. The famous Falls merited a mention in that day's journal entry.

"This morning before daylight I was up and at the Falls. I am, like most who have seen them, sensitively impressed with their grandeur". David delighted more with their surrounds. Over two hundred more words describe his botanising below.

Slowly, David retraced his steps back towards the Hudson, tasting the treasures of the land. Now it was Fall, the glory of the year. Only those who have experienced this phenomenon can appreciate the simple statement - "the forests are now seen to advantage, all the tints imaginable". Scientific travellers perhaps lack the verbosity of travel writers!

Albany was en fete that Sunday 5th October, when David Douglas returned to meet Governor De Witt Clinton. The town was in uproar with guns firing and music blaring. This was the celebrations to mark the completion of the Erie Canal.

Time and the future prosperity of New York would vindicate the celebration. David was delighted too. Acting on information, he found a fortune again.

"After a search of several hours I had the fortune to find it (Pterospora andromedia) in a ravine two miles south of Albany." He might have added, far from the din of the madding crowd.

Dr. Hosack had come up for the celebrations from New York. He and David dined with the Governor though he was still busy with official duties. However, there were other interesting people to meet. There was a Mr. Tracy, recommended by Clinton, as one who would aid David. Stephen Van Ransselaer, the wealthiest man in the United States, invited the botanist to breakfast and a tour of his garden and orchards. The patroon probably enjoyed his guest from Scotland as much as David was delighted with his host. Interest in his estate had only appeared after reading the works of Sir Walter Scott. Then he became an improver in the spirit of the Laird of Abbotsford.

Douglas records that "he has a large space of ground occupied as a pleasure or flower garden, which is a novelty in America, as little attention is paid to anything but what brings money or luxury to the table. His flower garden is kept in good order, under the direction of his daughters, with much taste." Scone and Scotland must have been recalled at the home of this disciple of Sir Walter Scott.

After other visits, David Douglas left Albany to meet General Morgan Lewis at his estate near Clairmont. The wild wood was now well behind him. Botanical exploration with all its excitement had to fall to his main project, procuring fruit trees. For the first time, the price of prospecting is mentioned, its origins perhaps in wet West Scotland.

"While at Albany I was seized with rheumatism in my knees, which almost reduced me from being able to do anything. Here I became lame for two days. I can never forget the attention paid to me by General Lewis and his family. On Wednesday and Thursday I was able to crawl about a little. I went with Mr. Lewis over the greater part of his estate. He pays great attention to agriculture and gardening; he has all the newest modes of tillage and many of the newest and most improved implements".

After a reunion with Mr. Thomson and a tour of his estate, it was down river to New York and a meeting of its Horticultural Society.

One last trip remained, a second pilgrimage to Philadelphia, the place of botanical heritage. Once again he met William Dick, the helpful janitor of the University. Some surviving specimens from the Lewis and Clark expedition flourished in his care. He also grew plants of the West brought back from the expedition of a Major Long during 1822. Most importantly, Dick introduced Douglas to a fellow spirit, Thomas Nuttal, the author of, A Journal of Travels to the Arkansa Territory during the Year 1819.

Thirteen years older than David, Thomas was an immigrant from England. A printer to trade, he worked in this city of a famous printer, Franklin. Time was taken off to travel and botanise. He helped print his first book, The Genera of North American Plants. Nuttal's knowledge, freely given, proved invaluable. There was a total meeting of minds, of men destined to be the two greatest botanical explorers of the North American Continent.

"In company with Mr. Nuttal I set out this morning to the residence of the late Mr. Bartram; his niece is a considerable botanist and draws well. Mr. Carr, to whom she is married, has but a moderate share of knowledge; this deficiency, however, is made up by his pleasing manner. In front of the house stands a very large cypress, 90 feet high and 23 round, planted by the first John Bartram; his son William (the late) held the tree while his father put the earth round; it is eighty-five years old".

How David Douglas would have enjoyed meeting the planter of that tree. John Bartram was ploughing when he was taken by the beauty of a daisy. By a strange coincidence, another contemporary ploughman was similarly smitten in Scotland. Robert Burns continued ploughing on and immortalised the "wee modest crimson-tipped flow'r" whose misfortune it had been to meet him in such an evil hour. Tradition tells that Bartram stopped and became a botanist after examining the little plant's intricate beauty. Learning Latin to enhance his education, he travelled the Indian country to collect specimens. By the Schuylkill River rose America's first botanic garden.

David Douglas returned to New York enriched indeed from this second visit to Philadelphia. For him it had been a city of botanical brotherly love. Now it was time to pack up the plants and go. Everyone was kindness itself with one exception, the Princes of Flushing. David's journal entries depict a deteriorating situation. Annoyed at not receiving the attention and orders they felt their establishment merited, father and son prevaricated.

12th November - "went to Flushing and returned in the evening. I must observe that Mr. Prince Jun., did not receive us with kindness but the reverse. If I can but obtain all the plants for the Society, I shall leave him for some other person".

17th November - "At Flushing and got part of the trees up. Could not get finished as Mr. Prince has not all the plants which are ardently needed".

4th December - Finished packing and everything on board on the 5th. I went to Flushing: our words were not of the most amicable tenor, and I am sorry to say that I must leave America without having good feelings toward every person".

The Princes were the exception. David Douglas was befriended and feted to the last. On the 9th he was to tell of his last day with Dr. Hosack.

"At his house was a large party of friends who kept mirth up till a late hour in the evening. In the course of the day General Lewis called, having come to town for the season; he has kindly invited me to visit him should I not sail".

Amongst the many kind friends mentioned in the journal, two were pre-eminent. They were specially worthy of note.

"The feelings of Dr. Hosack are already known. I cannot but say, at all times and in all cases, I found his very philanthropic mind unchanged, and his advice as to my own comfort. My feelings will never I hope, in any instance, speak but with gratefulness of Governor Clinton. I can say nothing more than that Dr. Hosack is a Clinton and Clinton a Hosack".

As well as those sentiments never destined for publication, David Douglas was to bestow on those two lovers of flora and benefactors of their fellow men, the ultimate accolade. For them, having their names entered in the rolls of botanical nomenclature must have amounted to a promise of immortality. He gave the world, Hosackia crassifolia and Clintonia elegans.

Leaving New York on the 10th December 1823, the sailing ship Nimrod brought back a precious cargo of plants for the London Horticultural Society. It also carried their greatest asset, David Douglas. In their wisdom they sent him West again.

CHAPTER THREE

West by Sea

"At twelve o'clock went on board the Hudson Bay Company's ship William and Anne, Captain Hanwell, bound for the Columbia River, north-west coast of America". Journal entry written by David Douglas on the 25th July 1824.

His Majesty's Ship Discovery, Captain Vancouver, sailed for the same coast thirty years before. She too carried a scientific traveller, another Scot from Perthshire, Archibald Menzies.

Both boys were born and bred by the banks of the River Tay. Both became apprentice gardeners on the estate of the local laird. Both left Perthshire to seek advancement at university-managed Botanic Gardens under eminent Professors. Both found fame by travelling to the greatest temperate rain forest in the world. Both are commemorated in the name of the greatest tree of that forest. Douglas Fir is the common name of this conifer. The classification of the botanical world identifies it as Pseudotsuga menziesii. Both botanists would have been pleased by this expression of the mutual respect they had for one another.

The mighty mountain ranges of the Rockies running north south, divide off the extreme western section of the North American continent. Parallel to them is a lesser range, the Pacific Mountain; from north to south named, the Coast Mountains of British Columbia, the Cascades of Washington and Oregon States, and the Sierra Nevada of California. They effectively define the Pacific coastal region.

Joel Garrow, a contemporary American writer, divides the continent into nine regions having a broad common geography and resulting identity of human settlement. The one which he believes has the best bio-geographical boundary, is the land west of the Pacific Mountain Range. He describes it as an ecological utopia and bestows the name, Ecotopia. Archibald Menzies and David Douglas would have applauded his designation.

The Pacific Maritime Forest extends along the coast from southern Alaska to San Francisco, California. At those extremities it is narrow and confined to the coast. It flourished at its ultimate, north and south of the Columbia River, the destination of the William and Anne. Here precipitation from the Pacific waters a coastal range of hills before bathing the western face of the Cascades. Coast, Coastal Range, Cascades, and the valley between are given the climatic conditions to create forest as a climax vegetation. Overall it was coniferous, broadleaves grew in select situations lower down. All species had evolved to their ultimate in appropriate sites. Lesser flora flourished within the forest, especially along its rivers.

Along the coast and up the rivers, an Indian people flourished. They were affluent without agriculture, the most advanced hunter gatherer society in the world. Satiated with salmon, clothed with fine furs, they lived in log houses. Heraldic art evolved from wood carving on door posts to the tall totems of last century.

The eighteenth century was almost over before Europeans entered Ecotopia. Spain had settled in southern California, Russians reached Alaska and quietly traded there. The vast sea coast awaited exploration when the ships of Captain Cook reached Nootka Sound on the west coast of Vancouver Island during 1778. Their principal remit was to find the fabled North West Passage across the continent. Cook's tragic death effectively ended the expedition. It returned via China. There, the crew found that furs, especially sea otter pelts, fetched a premium price. The Pacific fur trade pursued by many nations, especially Britain, ensued.

Spain surfaced from its long sleep and sent ships north to stop those incursions in her sphere of interest. At Nootka in 1789 a small settlement was seized and ships of the United Kingdom impounded. The British Government backed its citizens, Spain surrendered its sovereignty by signing the Nootka Convention of 1790.

The Naval Expedition commanded by Captain George Vancouver, 1791-6, was sent to implement the agreement and explore extensively. Sir Joseph Banks, Director of His Majesty's Garden at Kew, approached the Lords of the Admiralty seeking permission to send a scientific traveller with the expedition. To Vancouver's annoyance, they consented, and Archibald Menzies was encouraged to accept the post by Professor Hope of Edinburgh University.

Vancouver was vile to this unwelcome civilian. Fortunately, the young officers were kinder to the old Scottish botanist. He was their companion in the web of waterways as they explored the coast. Indians often terminated those trips when they decided to see off those visitors from afar.

Menzies Bay and Menzies Mountain are monuments on the coast of Menzies's passing. Menzies Island marks his ultimate penetration inland. The Expedition sought a mythical river which might give the desired North West Passage. They missed the major candidate. An American trader, Captain Gray found it and called it after his ship, the Columbia. The Chatham, a smaller ship of Vancouver's command, sailed upriver some months later. Point Vancouver and Menzies island recorded their progression.

When David Douglas visited Archibald Menzies before leaving, his predecessor was about seventy years old. Despite his scholarly description of the feast of flora, no further British botanist had followed. To Menzies, the event must have been a dream come true. He would have expected his successor to be Scottish, most scientific travellers were Scots. That he was from Perthshire must have been perfect, and a Taysider. Only forty miles separated Scone from Styx.

Scotland was also the home of most who sought furs across the continent of North America. The Hudson Bay Company ships sailed for centuries from Stromness in Orkney with new recruits. Scottish soldiers settled in Quebec after the rule of France fell in 1763. Many became partners in the fur trade pushing further north west. The North West Company of Montreal evolved and sent new recruits further out. One such, Alexander MacKenzie, crossed the Rockies during 1793 and paddled to the Pacific. Eight years later, Simon Fraser explored the land he crossed and named it New Caledonia. Following south, he followed the Fraser River to the sea. It was too treacherous for a fur trade highway. David Thomson found that when he canoed the Columbia from its source to the sea in 1811. Scots awaited him there.

Alexander MacKenzie had published an account of his travels as well as petitioning the British Government to extend the Empire to the Pacific Ocean with no success. President Jefferson read MacKenzie and acted. The Lewis and Clark Expedition crossed the Continental Divide and reached the mouth of the Columbia in 1805. (David Douglas had seen some of its plants procured, when in Philadelphia).

John Jacob Astor, the successful giant of the New York fur trade, decided to beat the North West Company to the Columbia. He recruited from their Scots and sent a ship round Cape Horn. It arrived early in April 1811.

David Thomson was welcomed at the freshly constructed Fort Astoria on the 15th of July 1811. A man MacDougal was in charge, with the Stuarts from West Perthshire under him. All was far from well, their ship was off trading up the coast with others. Its crazy captain brought disaster by exposing it to an Indian attack.

A year later, a second ship came and left. War was now in progress between the United States and the United Kingdom. A North West party arrived armed and took the Fort. Now renamed Fort George, it carried on to the amalgamated North West and Hudson Bay Company after 1821.

David Douglas sailed round the Horn as 1824 changed to 1825. Dr. John Scouler, the ship's surgeon was a fellow pupil of Dr. Hooker. They botanised ashore when stops permitted. On the 12th of February 1825, the William Anne reached the latitude of the Columbia River. Storms stopped penetration for seven weeks.

CHAPTER FOUR

Entry To Ecotopia

"On Sunday the 3rd, at daybreak, Cape Disappointment was seen at 28 miles distant".

That April day it seemed the long voyage would end but once again the William and Anne had to pull out to sea. No channel was visible, breakers broke over the breadth of bar.

Six days later they entered the river mouth and dropped anchor on the north shore, Baker's Bay. Several shots of the ship's cannon were fired to attract the attention of the people in Fort George, situated seven miles upriver. Surprisingly they found no response, a cause for concern. Despite this David Douglas delayed no longer.

"The rain on Friday fell in torrents. On Saturday the 9th, the doctor and I went on shore in Baker's Bay, where immediately on stepping of the boat we found Rubus spectabilis and Gaultheria shallon growing close to the water's edge. We picked many plants only known to us in the herbaria, others only by name".

"On stepping on the shore, Gaultheria shallon was the first plant I took in my hands. So pleased was I that I could scarcely see anything for it. Mr. Menzies correctly observes that it grows under thick pine forests in great luxuriance and would make a valuable addition to our gardens. It grows most luxuriantly on the margins of the woods, particularly near the ocean".

David Douglas never failed to give credit to his predecessor from Perthshire. A generation apart, they were boys who botanised by the banks of the Tay in youth. Thousands of miles west, they were in spirit united on the Columbia.

"With truth I may count this one of the happiest days of my life." The entry must have been all the better for the congenial companionship of Dr. Scoular. A letter to Professor Hooker paints a pleasing picture of those two fine young men exulting in that ancient forest environment.

"His departure I much regret; we had always been friends and here our friendship increased. When botanising along the shores of the Columbia River, and in the adjoining woods, we would sometimes sit down and rest our limbs and the conversation often turned to Glasgow and Ben Lomond. If a favourite moss caught his eye, it was eagerly grasped and transferred to the vasculum and the remark was pretty sure to follow - How much would Dr. Hooker like to be with us."

Extent of main journey made from
Fort Vancouver during 1825.

On their return from their first excursion, they met their first native Americans and a servant of the Scots who officered the Hudson Bay Company.

"On returning to the ship we found that a Canadian had been sent from the establishment, accompanied by some natives, with fresh provisions for us. Several canoes of Indians visited the ship and behaved in a civil manner, bringing dried salmon, fresh sturgeon, and dried berries of various kinds, which they readily gave in exchange for trinkets, molasses, and bread."

This perfect picture introduces the world David Douglas was now to inhabit. A Frenchman from Quebec, the Canada of that time, one of a race of voyageurs who paddled the canoes of the Company across the lakes and rivers of the Continent, would often be his immediate aide. Most often, Native Americans would be his guides. From the first they fascinated him.

"The practice of compressing the forehead, of perforating the septum of the nose and ears with shells, bits of copper wire, beads, or in fact any hardware, gives a stranger a curious idea of their singular habits."

A few days later the William and Anne sailed upriver for several miles to Fort George. No gun had replied to their signal because the fort was finished as a service station. Nothing remains today and no reconstruction on site is possible. The town of Astoria covers all and commemorates the name of Astor's establishment, of the first American presence. Not surprisingly the name of the King was consigned to oblivion. The new Hudson Bay company had decided to replace the Northwester's base with a greater one upriver, Fort Vancouver.

David Douglas now met his first fellow Scot of the fur trade, Alexander McKenzie. One of the many bearing that name, he was not one of the greats who left a legend behind. Receiving the traveller kindly, he told of the impending arrival of the Chief Factor of Columbia.

Dr. John McLoughlan was a legend in his lifetime, one of the great figures of the fur trade. Tall and impressive, he was the powerful patriarch of the Pacific province of the Hudson Bay Company Empire. Flowing white hair earned him the title, White Headed Eagle, from the Indians. They respected his firm though benevolent rule.

A former factor of the North West Company, his fur trade credentials were impeccable. American historians honour his name, proclaiming him to be the Father of the Oregon. Many owed him much, not least David Douglas.

"On Saturday, 16th April, the chief factor, John McLoughlan Esq., came down the river from the new establishment, who received me with much kindness.

I showed him my instructions and informed him verbally the object of my voyage, and talked over my pursuit."

David for a second time sailed up a major river of North America. The contrast across the continent was total. This river road inland, through uncleared complete forest, was the Hudson as Henry of that name had seen it in 1609. It was the Tay in Scotland as seen by Mesolithic Man nine millennia before. The canoe, hollowed from a tree trunk, was similar to those used then, an example was excavated at Perth.

Six people paddled, Indians with no real food, for forty miles against the current. Small wonder they sat round the fire that night relishing a roasted sturgeon of around 26 pounds weight. David and the Doctor dined more fastidiously on some sturgeon, tea, and a slice of bread. They slept in the canoe and sailed on at three in the morning. Nineteen hours later they arrived at their destination, the site of the new Fort, over seventy miles from the sea amid spectacular scenery.

"The scenery from this place is sublime - high wooded hills, mountains covered with perpetual snow, extensive natural meadows and plains of deep alluvial deposits covered with a rich sward of grass and a profusion of flowering plants. The most remarkable mountains are Mounts, Hood, St. Helens, Vancouver, and Jefferson, which are at all seasons covered in snow as low down as the summit of the hills by which they are surrounded."

The sylvan scene is long gone, but the sheer beauty of the mountains, the Cascades, survives as David described. Their glory endures to inspire those who lift their eyes towards them.

Today a city called Vancouver surrounds the site of the Fort of that name. The captain of King George's ship possessed a name that was allowed to endure in a State called after George Washington. The fort of fur traders became a United States military establishment until the second half of this century.

Demilitarisation allowed the opportunity to reconstruct the original. This restoration has been achieved to perfection. With their profound respect for heritage, the National Parks Service of the United States excelled in authenticity. Archaeological investigation preceded construction. Posts were put back in the original holes dug out over a century plus before. Today's traveller enters excellence in detail. Blue beads, beloved of the Indians, sell from the same source of manufacture. A blacksmith, dressed as the past, toils over a real forge. He relates to the present in his product only. Useful metalwork for the Parks service replaces the traps of the traders. The style and content of the Chief Factor's House reflect the standing of this urbane man who wore black clothes and carried a gold headed cane.

The author by the Monument before its refurbishment.

The Douglas Fir at Scone Palace grown from the seed sent from the Columbia River during 1826.

Douglas Fir, over 800 years old, Cathedral Grove on Vancouver Island.

The Hoh River Valley, a pristine preserved area of the temperate rain forest.

Sitka Spruce dominant in a wet world of mosses and ferns beside the Hoh River.

An early illustration of the interior of the large log houses of the coastal Indian tribes.

Fort Vancouver as it had developed by the time of David Douglas's second visit or later.

Old Scone 1837, the medieval market cross, former entrance and through it the present Palace.

"In the river opposite my hut lies Menzies Island, so named by Mr. Broughton in honour of Archibald Menzies, Esq., then his companion on the famous expedition. On my arrival a tent was kindly offered, having no houses yet built, which I occupied for some weeks; a lodge of deerskin was then made for me which soon became too small by the augmenting of my collection and being ill-adapted for drying my plants and seeds. I am now August 16 in a hut made of bark of Thuya occidentalis which most likely will be my winter lodging."

On the first of May, the first foray into the forest was made by David Douglas. On the second he visited Menzies Island. Its low sandy but rich soil hosted a plethora of plants. One, Mysotis, was particularly interesting. Its name made this a particularly Scottish site. "This very interesting species was found on Menzies Island in company with Mr. Scouler, who agreed with me to call it Mysotis Hookeri after Dr. Hooker of Glasgow." Forays for flora often passed the places used by the First Nation.

"Passed several Indian steaming huts or vapour baths; a small hole is dug about 1 foot deep, in which hot stones are placed and water thrown on them so as to produce steam; the bather then goes in naked and remains until well steamed; he immediately plunges into some pool or river, which is chosen not to be far distant. They are formed of sticks, mud, and turfs, with a small hole for means of entering. They are most frequently used when the natives come from their hunting parties, after the fatigues of war, and also before they go on any expedition which required bodily exertion. My curiosity was not so strong as to regale myself with a bath."

After David denied himself this delight, he shot down river to the ship and retrieved the remainder of his belongings. Dr. Scouler's short visit upriver was over, the ship now sailed north to trade up the coast. The slower return journey produced plants of seventy five species, a few birds and insects, and four quadrupeds. Although plants were paramount, this scientific traveller had many remits.

Perhaps it was the immediate feeling of separation from this fine friend that came to mind when he found a mimulus. Botanical benefices were bestowed on others by David Douglas, not on himself.

"This interesting species I call M. Scouleri, after John Scouler, who had been the agreeable companion of my long voyage from England and walks on the Columbia."

"Tuesday, May 31st - Made a journey of three days on the north banks of the river towards the Rapids, accompanied by one Indian belonging to a tribe called Kyuse; his name was 'Yes', I mean his Indian name; he had no good qualifications except being a good huntsman."

This expedition on foot, with the positively named though unqualified assistant, was a prelude to a greater one upriver. By now it had dawned on David how vast was the field and how rich the harvest to be reaped. How to spend his time to best account was becoming increasingly important. He was persuaded by the Chief Factor not to sail on the ship to Nootka on Vancouver Island, because of troubles with the local Indians. It was a pity that this place of Archibald Menzies was denied. Instead, he was assured that crossing the continent with a Company party would be possible. An inland interest now appeared and an expedition presented an opportunity for initial exploration.

"June 20th - Towards midday left my residence for a journey up the river in company with the canoes going to the different posts in the interior, a few miles above the Great Falls, about a hundred miles from the ocean."

The current was strong as the river was swollen by melting snow. The paddler's progress was slow against such odds. David records that he botanised on the banks where they were unobstructed by timber or rocks. He does not record the paddler's view of their passenger's peculiar ways.

"The second day we passed the Grand Rapids, forty six miles above the Fort. The scenery at this place is romantic and wild, with high mountains on each side clothed with timber of immense seize". This euphoric view of the forest formed by the balmy Pacific climate was soon to be replaced.

"From the Grant Rapids to the Great Falls (70 miles) the banks are steep, rocky, and in places rugged. This hills diminish in elevation, and are thinly clothed with stunted timber, the shrubs only a few feet high. We are no longer fanned by the huge pine, thuya or Acer, or regaled by Populus tremuloides for ever quivering in the breeze. As far as the eye can stretch is one dreary waste of barren soil thinly clothed with herbage."

Outward exploration from the river confirmed David's initial assessment of the rain-shadow country east of the Pacific Mountain chain. He was out of Ecotopia indeed.

"Nothing but extensive plains and barren hills, with the greater part of the herbage scorched and dead by the intense heat. I had to cross a plain nineteen miles without a drop of water, of pure white sand, thermometer in the shade 97%." Broiled and blistered, he botanised where flora existed. Some ground plant colonised this unpromising environment. The outcome of the trip overall was rewarding. He summed up his botanical inventory by writing that "in this journey many fine plants were secured."

"July 19th - Early in the morning I left my residence in a small canoe, with one Canadian and two Indians for a journey to the shores of the ocean, principally for the purpose of searching for and enquiring after the tuberous-rooted Cyperus mentioned by Pursh in his preface, the root of which is said to afford the natives something like potatoes when boiled." The Lewis and Clarke expedition had described this useful vegetable, David was intrigued.

This first little expedition personally led by David Douglas was not a success. Twelve wet windy days spent north of the entrance to the river resulted in little profit. It was a salutary lesson on survival in this wet waste, even for a Scot.

"Now I have a little idea of travelling without the luxuries of life. Only two nights were dry during my stay on the shore; before I could lie down to sleep my blanket drying generally occupied an hour." He travelled on tea, it became his staff of life.

The plants he had sought in vain were to be found south of the river mouth. Troubles between the tribes prevented initial inquiry. However, David descended the river again to seek Indian assistance.

Native Americans still dominated the land. However helpful the Hudson Bay expeditions might be along the Columbia River, David Douglas decided that inland must be with the Indians. The secret of his success lay in his appreciation of them. He showed no fear of the fiercest and befriended the friendly.

"The natives are inquisitive in the extreme, treacherous, and will pillage and murder when they can do it with impunity. Most of the tribes of the coast the Chenooks, Clatsaps, Clikitats, and Killimucks from the association they have with Europeans are anxious to imitate them and are on the whole not unfriendly. Some of them are by no means deficient of ability."

This early entry of his journal was now to be tested by seeking out a chief called "Cockqua, the principal chief of the Chenooks and Chochalii tribes, who is exceedingly fond of all the chiefs that come from King George." Archibald Menzies writing back to Sir Joseph Banks often rejoiced in procuring plants which would grace "His Majesty's Garden." Douglas did not directly collect for Kew, but had similar if less direct royal supplier status. The Indian Chiefs certainly accorded him respect as a subject of the Great White Chief.

Cockqua received David Douglas royally. A sturgeon, that Royal fish of Scotland, was displayed and its choicest cuts offered by the gracious host to his guest, who recorded the repast with relish.

"In justice to my Indian friend, I cannot say but he afforded me the most comfortable meal I had for a considerable time before, from the spine and head of the fish."

Cockqua had constructed a small cabin for David within his large lodge, a communal house occupied by his extended family. This kind act had considerable merit as the tribe expected a Cladsap commando raid across the river that night. Fear of flies in the lodge led David to decline this lodging and retire to his tent. Possibly viewed as fearlessness in the face of the expected enemy, his stock rose. Hostilities, however, did not ensue.

"In the evening about three hundred men in their war garments danced the war dance and sung several death songs, which to me alone imparted an indescribable sensation. The following day seventeen canoes of warriors, nearly four hundred men, made their appearance, when, after several harangues, hostilities were for the present suspended".

Peace by the Pacific now established, like the Highland Clans of Scotland, the tribes turned to treats. An arrogant archer put an arrow through a small hoop of grass, six inches in diameter, when in the air. He also displayed some ability with his rifle. No chief of King George could shoot like him. David downed an eagle in the wing to acclaim. The boaster threw up his hat and saw it reduced to the brim in mid air. No doubt delighted, "Cockqua said 'Cladsap cannot shoot like you.'".

David Douglas must have been an enigma to the Indians. Trading they understood, it had always existed between the coastal and inland people. Traders from the ships gave them alcohol for premium pelts. The good Dr. McLoughlan did not and found it harder to procure his programme. Furs were what the white men wanted. This new one looked only to leaves and plants. David left with a floral selection and some artefacts, included was the Chief's own hat

"August 19th - Towards afternoon left in a small canoe with one Canadian and two Indians, in company with a party of men going on a hunting excursion southward, on a visit to the Multnomah River, one of the southern branches of the Columbia."

This expedition up the present Willamette came after a fortnight at the Fort mainly spent sorting out the proceeds of the previous trip. Rain had been heavy and the river was initially an extension of the Columbia. The banks were covered with Douglas Fir, Silver Fir, Oak, and Poplar, growing on the richest soil he had seen.

Thirty six miles upriver were the Falls, forty three feet high and difficult to pass. Three hours were spent hauling up the canoes.

"Two days more took me to the village of the Calapooie nation, a peaceful good-disposed people, twenty—four miles above the falls, where my camp was formed for several days."

The Calapooies cultivated their own tobacco. Plantations were placed far into the forest and kept secret. After searching, David found such a secret location. Returning with specimens and seeds, he met the owner. Initial anger towards the botanist was mitigated by a present of tobacco brought from Europe. They smoked together and discussed the merits of cultivation. However, the Calapooies had a greater tale to tell.

"In the tobacco pouches of the Indian I found the seeds of a remarkably large pine which they eat as nuts, and from whom I learned it existed in the mountains to the south. No time was lost in ascertaining the existence of this grand tree, which I named Pinus Lambertiana, but no perfect seed could I find."

David Douglas decided that he would not return to Britain without this prince of pines. Time at present was precious as the William and Anne would soon return from Nootka. He had to harvest seeds seen earlier for onward dispatch home.

"On September 5th, having engaged a chief as my guide and accompanied by one Canadian, I left on a journey to the Grand Rapids."

Chief Chumtalia does not appear for posterity in a very favourable light. David's decision to climb high in the Cascades may have come as an unpleasant surprise.

"On Saturday morning, when Chumtalia learned that it was my wish and intention to visit the summit of the mountains on the north side of the river, he became forthwith sick, and soon found an excuse for exempting himself from this undertaking. He, however, sent a younger brother instead, accompanied by two young men of the village."

Three days were spent on the ascent, one of the most laborious undertakings David had at that date. After a freezing night spent on the barren summit, Douglas descended to camp faint and weary. Two days were required to recuperate before he went for the south side.

"In two days I got my guide Chumtalia to attend me to the mountain on the south side of the river, which he did most willingly. I found this easier of ascent, and reached the top after a laborious march of fifteen hours. I had the good fortune to find two new species of pines, Pinus nobilis and Pinus amabilis, two of the noblest species of the tribe."

David Douglas did not exaggerate when he first mentions those Silver Firs. Noble Silver Fir, now classified as Abies procera is a beautiful bluish tree. Abies amabilis, the Lovely Fir, is well worthy of that name.

Back at Fort Vancouver was young Scouler returned from the trading trip. What tales they had to tell. "We sat and talked over our several journeys unconscious of time, until the sun, from behind the majestic mountains warned us that a new day had come." No sun would ever set on those sons of Scotland and their Pacific North West.

The remainder of this month was devoted to packing up my gleanings of dried plants, consisting sixteen large bundles of American and eight from other places, a large chest of seeds, one of birds and quadrupeds, and one of various articles of dress etc. A portion of each of the varieties of seeds was reserved for the purpose of sending across the continent in the ensuing spring".

Somewhere was seed for Scone in Scotland. The story of that venerable Douglas Fir standing near the medieval cross, within sight of the Palace, started here.

Right in the midst of this crucial time, disaster struck. David fell on a rusty nail when employed in packing the last of the boxes, a large abscess formed on the knee-joint. It was almost November before he set off down river with four Indians, hoping to say farewell to Scouler.

"I left the establishment in company with the late Mr. Alexander McKenzie and a small canoe and four Indians. A boisterous westerly wind obliged us to camp at the junction of the River Mulnomah, having made only twenty miles progress. The following day we proceeded, and at eight at night reached the village of Oak Point, where I had a letter given to me from my friend Dr. Scouler, who informed me that they would probably be in the river for some days longer."

They struggled on through a gale, even having to haul the canoe over headland. The ship sailed, lost by only one hour. A dejected David Douglas must have looked sadly seaward.

Now he was alone among the Indians. McKenzie had been left at his station, no Canadian voyageur was available for this trip. He slept in the village of Con Comly, chief of the Chinooks, on the north side of the Columbia River. There he met another from further north, Tha-a-muxi or the Beard. He offered his company to David and they set off in style in one of the great canoes of the coast paddled by twelve warriors. Even it almost floundered, and a portage was necessary over Cape Disappointment at the mouth of the river.

The Beard was a congenial companion. Unlike his fellows he had forsworn alcohol because of youthful indiscretion. Tobacco substituted, and smoking stupor occurred five times daily. David found him an expensive companion.

"Long ere daylight we were ready to leave Cape Foulweather, which name it truly deserves, and we walked along the sandy beach to Whitbey Harbour, where we found the village deserted, our prospect not in the least bettered."

At sea again they had travelled through a hurricane of rain and sleet. David's leg was stiff and painful after the exertion of pulling the canoe overland. Cold, wet, and hungry, he crawled on sustained only by two ounces of chocolate.

"I spent this night at the fire. On Saturday I found myself so broken down and my knee so much worse that I did not stir out for the whole of the day."

It must have appeared to David that his end was near as he lay in his hut of pine branches on the sodden shore. However, the very hurricane came to his aid. Ducks driven inland crossed the camp. He felled five with one shot. His companions cooked them without plucking, one ate his raw. David dined on duck and his ever necessary tea. The fire also attracted the Beard's people from the other side of the bay. A canoe crossed and carried them back.

"I reached my guide's village a little before dusk, where I had every kindness and all the hospitality Indian courtesy could suggest, and made a stay of several days at his house."

Today a town called Aberdeen stands where David Douglas received sanctuary from the storms. This settlement, with its Scottish name, seems to symbolise the first Scot who was befriended by the First Nation. A year before, Douglas had been a worthy representative of his people among the great of the East. Now he was able successfully, to relate alone, to the inhabitants of the West of the continent. This young person of Perthshire, a product of a simple faith, had a country background embracing labourers and lairds. His charitable outlook and professionalism was without constraint.

David Douglas left this cruel coast on the 7th of November 1825 and journeyed inland up a river which ran directly west to the ocean, the Chehalis, (his Cheecheeler). His kind host came with him as far as the inevitable cascades, some sixty miles from the sea. David now had to cross over to the Pacific Valley and another river which flowed south to the Columbia, the Cowlitz, (his Cow-a-lidsk). The time had come to take leave of his friend Chief Tha-a-muxi, the Beard, who had one favour to ask.

"Before leaving me he requested that I would shave him, as he had pretensions to civilisation and aped with nicety European manners. I accordingly did so, and invited him to come at the New Year to see me, when I would give him a dram, a smoke, and shave him again. He told me before he left, to let all King George's chiefs know of him, when I spoke to them with paper."

David Douglas gave good Tha-a-muxi more than that. His journal entry ensured a place for him in time to come. The replacement guide was the converse.

"At the village where I put up I bargained with an Indian to carry my baggage on his horse to the Cow-a-lidsk River, one of the northern branches of the Columbia. I had some difficulty with this fellow in accomplishing my end; he was the most mercenary rascal I have seen. I had to give him twenty shots of ammunition, two feet of tobacco, a few flints, and a little vermilion."

Rain, rain, and more rain, was a continuing impediment to progress. David details the weary wetness. Little creeks and rivulets were so much swollen that his clothes were often off three times a day swimming across some of them. At last he reached the river and respite.

"My track was along the foot of Mount St. Helens of Vancouver, which lay a little way to the north-east. At Schachanaway's or the chief of the Chinook tribe's house I learned he had just returned from a trading visit from other parts and had brought with him a bag of potatoes, flour, a little molasses, and rum, all of which had a portion and a comfortable night's lodging."

Furnished again by the First Nation, he sailed alone down river to the Columbia in a small boat. Now the rain giving a rapid river worked in his favour. By mid-afternoon he was at the Columbia confluence, camping overnight on an island. Leaving was a problem, an ebb-tide beached the boat and his strength was not sufficient to shift her over the sands. Eventually afloat, David sailed upriver using his blanket and cloak for good purpose.

"I arrived again at Fort Vancouver at half-past eleven at night, being absent twenty-five days, during which I experienced more fatigue and misery, and gleaned less than in any trip I have had in the country."

Perhaps it was poor in plants, but surely large in life. David Douglas was now a Northwester. Like his fellow Scots of the fur trade he had become an adventurer. Now under Hudson Bay Company rule, these men had crossed the continent while their former rivals slept by the frozen sea. The lords of lake and forest still felt free.

David's December entry is devoted to one newly arrived. Alexander Rodrick McLeod lead the party which had left Hudson Bay on the 21st of July to cross the Rockies to the Columbia

"At midday on the 18th the express, consisting of two boats and forty men arrived from Hudson's Bay which they left on the 21st of July. They were observed at the distance of some miles, rapidly descending the stream. In this distant land where there is only one annual post, they were by every person made most welcome guests."

No mail arrived for David. This time the express had not been able to wait the arrival of the Hudson Bay Company Ship from Britain. His mail was a continent away, a great disappointment, but perhaps fuelling his feeling of freedom. There was news of other Scots abroad, fellow scientific searchers.

"A Mr. McLeod, the person in charge of the party, told me he met Captain Franklin's party on Cumbernauld Lake on their way to Bear Lake, their winter residence, early in July; their stay being only a few minutes Dr. Richardson did not write to me.

I learned that there was a Mr. Drummond attached to them as a botanist: he accompanied Mr. McLeod as far on his route as the foot of the Rocky Mountains, and is to pass the summer in the country towards Peace and Smoky Rivers. This I take to be Drummond of Forfar, from the description given of him."

Alexander Rodrick had spent the previous five years at Fort Good Hope on the MacKenzie River. He met Indians who had traded with the Russians and firmly believed that there was a North West Passage. He impressed David as a man of perseverance, one who had visited the Polar Sea, the Atlantic and Pacific Oceans, in the short space of eleven months."

"On the 24th December the rain fell in such torrents, without the least intermission, that my little hut of Thuya bark, which stood in rather a low situation, was completely inundated; 14 inches of water was in it. As my lodgings were not of the most comfortable sort, Mr. McLoughlan kindly invited me to part of his house in a half-finished state. Therefore on Christmas Day all my things were removed to my new dwelling. After the morning service was performed, they took an airing on horseback. I was prevented from joining them in their pleasant excursion because of my troublesome knee."

So 1825 drew to a close, a year in which by his own calculations David Douglas had travelled over two thousand miles. Since his April arrival, he had followed the footsteps his Perthshire predecessor and far beyond. Travels over rough terrain had taken its toll. His journal entries suggest permanent pain. New Year is a mystic time for Scots. At home it is often a dark damp day of foreboding. David Douglas saw 1826 arrive in a log fort standing at the edge of deep gloomy woodland beside a raging river. Scone and Scotland so far away as to be lost forever. His initial entry in his journal could only express those feelings.

"Sunday, January 1st - Commenced a year in such a far removed corner of the earth, where I am nearly destitute of civilised society, there is some scope for reflection. In 1824, I was on the Atlantic on my way to England; 1825 between the island of Juan Fernandez and the Galapagos in the Pacific; I am now here, and God only knows where I may be next. In all probability, if a change does not take place, I will shortly be consigned to the tomb. I can die satisfied with myself. I never have given cause for remonstrance or pain to an individual on earth. I am in my twenty-seventh year."

Despite his dismal entry, 1826 was to be his annus mirabilis. David Douglas decided his destiny alone. His employers were informed of his decision to remain and reap the harvest here. The eventual road home would be by Hudson Bay.

CHAPTER FIVE

Beyond The Cascades

"From what I have seen of this country, and what I have been enabled to do, there is still much to be done; after a careful consideration as to the propriety of remaining for a season longer than instructed to do, I have resolved not to leave for another year to come."

David Douglas decided, despite his affliction, to remain in this ecological utopia. He details the debate in his own mind before reaching this momentous decision. Self sacrifice in the interest of science helped his justification. He was prepared to labour for little. "Most cheerfully will I labour this year without any remuneration, if I get only the wherewith to purchase a little clothing." Even this necessity, he soon sacrificed.

"March 20th - Having resolved to devote a season in the interior parts of the country skirting the Rocky Mountains, Dr. McLoughlin, who was unremitting with his kind attentions, allowed me to embark in the spring boat for the interior with two reams of paper, which was an enormous indulgence. Rather than go unprovided in this respect I curtailed the small supply of clothing."

They set off in some style, all except David dressed in their best. Pipes played and the Chief Factor officially wished them well. The departure of the brigade for Hudson Bay was a special occasion. Soon there was a stop to change clothes, the voyageurs packed away their 'braws' for another time.

Up the then untamed river Columbia were three obstacles to progress, the Grand Rapids, the Dalles, and the Great Falls. The party portaged the first and camped under a shelving rock at the second. The magic of the mountains moved David.

"The scenery at this season is likewise grand beyond description; the high mountains in the neighbourhood, which are for the most part covered in pines of several species, some of which grow to an enormous size, are all loaded with snow.... the reflection from the snow on the mountains, together with the vivid green of the gigantic pines, form a contrast of rural grandeur that can scarcely be surpassed."

Daybreak at the Dalles proved to be less pleasant. They found themselves surrounded by 450 Indians, David uncharacteristically calls them "savages", who seemed anything but amicable. A tribute of tobacco helped to calm them. Four miles further on were the Falls and further trouble. Tobacco tribute did not suffice. John McLeod, the brigade leader, found himself with an arrow in a drawn bow against his chest. David presented his gun at the brave and dared him to fire.

Journey beyond the Cascade Mountains during 1826.

Fortunately, a friendly Cayuse chief intervened and diffused the situation. David decided to better McLeod's tobacco tribute to their benefactor.

"I being King George's Chief or the Grass Man as I am called, I bored a hole in the only shilling I had, one which had been in my pocket since I left London, and, the septum of his nose being perforated, I suspended it to him with a brass wire. this was to him the great seal of friendship."

Across the North American Continent at that time, a wealthy young man, James Fenimore Cooper, was writing fiction. His Leatherstocking Tales, based on a forgotten past delighted his readers at home and abroad. David Douglas and his fellow Scots were playing real roles.

Despite the delighted Chief's promise of continued protection, the party slept little that night. Rain was heavy, sleet swept over them. David's knee was troublesome and stiff. Despite those difficult circumstances, by the light of a taper he wrote Professor Hooker. When this letter reached Glasgow, the recipient could never have envisaged the environment in which it was composed. Their mutual wet West Scotland excursions were tame by comparison.

"Clear, fine, warm weather.......At three o'clock on the 28th arrived at Walla Walla establishment, where I was very friendly received by S. Black, Esq., the person in charge. The whole country from the Great Falls to this place is nearly destitute of timber. Dry gravely soils, with extensive plains."

Once again David was out of Ecotopia and into the arid hinterland east of the Cascade Mountains, at the centre of the Pacific Mountain Chain. This part of the rain shadow country is today called the Columbia Basin. Its eastern rim is the Rocky Mountains. In David's day it was a desert mitigated only by the Columbia and its tributaries. However, the Pacific rains penetrated inland in places high enough to receive them.

Black baked in the furnace of Fort Walla Walla, a strategic post south of the Snake River's juncture with the Columbia. Here Douglas looked south and saw a ridge of high snowy mountains, recipients of that rain. Black promised help to get to those Blue Mountains during June.

The brigade proceeded upriver, with David walking along the banks, flat in this great plain. He was to write, "this part of the country is entirely destitute of timber; soil, light brown earth, sandy and gravely on the banks of the rivers, and blown in some places into hills or mounds 50 to 60 feet high." On the 1st of April 1826, a second letter was sent to Glasgow, recipient Dr. Scouler. No doubt David's companion on the Columbia was amazed by the changed country it traversed east of the Cascades.

"13th, Thursday - busy copying the remainder of my notes, as Mr. McLeod is to leave early in the morning for his long trip to Hudson's Bay. I am particularly obliged also to this gentleman for his friendly attention. He has in the most careful manner taken my small box of seeds in his own private box and will hand it over to Mr. McTavish."

Perhaps this special seed consignment included seed of Douglas Fir for Scone in Scotland. When, a year later, David Douglas himself endured the hazards of the route across the Rockies, he would be even more fulsome in noting McLeod's kindness.

Now in the company of the commandant of the interior, John Warren Dease, David journeyed on upriver. Now he was nearing new country to the east.

"The whole country is very mountainous and rugged, the nearer the Rocky Mountains more so, and more thickly wooded, of three species of Pinus...On the plains and valleys there is a thick sward of grass."

Back in botanist's territory, he saw his first American Larch and found Pinus ponderosa. Flowers now fill his journal entries. Kettle Falls on the Columbia was especially attractive. The long journey of almost six hundred miles to Fort Colville was well worth the effort expended. Dease helped Douglas in many ways. When David's gun required repairing, he sent him with three of his best horses and two hunters to see old Jacob Finlay at Spokane, seventy miles away. Before returning to Fort Colville by the Kettle Falls, an inland Indian custom was observed.

"Close to the old establishment an Indian burying-ground is to be seen, certainly one of the most curious spectacles I have seen in this country. All the property of the dead, consisting of war implements, garments, gambling articles, in fact everything. Even the favourite horse of the departed is shot with his bow and arrow, and his skin with hoofs and skull hung over the remains of the deceased owner."

On June 5th David Douglas left the "wild romantic scenery of Kettle Falls" to go downriver by Fort Okanagon to Walla Walla. The lure of those mystic Blue Mountains could no longer be denied.

At Okanagan, David met another Douglas, of future fame. James of that name, had been born in Demerara of a Scots father and Mullato mother. He was sent home to Scotland to be educated at Lanark. This highly intelligent product of the Empire, rose in the Hudson Bay Company, was knighted by the Queen Empress, and became Her Majesty's first Governor of British Columbia. Because of his prominence in the Pacific North West, the name Douglas Fir is often erroneously attributed to him.

David travelled with him, his superior William Connelly, Chief Factor of New Caledonia, and other officers. The brigade of five boats flew downriver eager to reach their destination. David was dropped off at Walla Walla wearied and ready to sleep on the floor of Indian Hall. The eternal flies forced him to flee outside. Here also, a higher form of fauna also pestered him.

"Last night I was much annoyed by a herd of pack rats which devoured every article of seed I had collected, cut a bundle of dry plants almost right through, carried off my razor and soap-dish. One, as he was in the act of depriving me of my inkstand, which I had just been using before I lay down and was lying close to my pillow, I lifted my gun (which is my night companion as well as my day, and lies generally alongside me, the muzzle to my feet) and gave him the contents."

David the scientist describes the rat and deplores not reloading with smaller shot. This he did after daybreak and with characteristic patience, waited their return. He was rewarded with a smaller specimen . An Indian's arrival with mail from Fort Vancouver which had arrived by the annual ship, brought back the old world.

"I grasped the parcel eagerly and tore it open turning over my letters. Never in my life did I feel in such a state; an uneasy, melancholy, but pleasing sensation stole on my mind, with an inordinate longing for the remaining part, and although I did not hear from my friends, I now for once in my life enjoy and relish the luxury of hearing from England....for in this uninhabited land the post calls but seldom."

Dr. McLoughlin had prudently retained the main mail, not entirely trusting the Indian. David decided to get going towards the Blue Mountains. Difficulties arose over language differences. A voyageur's son, the Young Wasp, was required to interpret with the Indian guide. The latter required that his family be fed in his absence and much more.

"Afterwards a pair of shoes, and, as his leggings were much worn, leather to make new ones was necessary; a scalping knife, a small piece of tobacco, and a strip of red coarse cloth to make an ornamental cap. This occupied two hours and was sealed with volumes of smoke from a large pipe."

Black provided provisions and three horses, eventually the trio travelled south. They crossed a virtual desert and had to climb to the middle of the mountain to meet the tree line. Soon snow was a problem for David, who left behind his less enthusiastic followers. Worse still was wind, rain and hail as he reached the summit. This was a summer storm of thunder and lightening. David was driven downhill to find his companions damp in body and spirit.

Somewhere over the hills was believed to be a hidden valley. The voyageurs called it, the Grande Ronde. They invested it with a tranquil and benign climate, a second Eden. Douglas desired to find it, but this time had to forego. The Young Wasp proved treacherous, depressing the guide's morale with poisonous fiction. Eventually the Indian escaped to avoid being "turned into a grizzly bear". A second expedition with other Indians also proved fruitless.

Maybe fatigue and frustration made the missing mail even more important at this time. David decided to go down the river for it. He met a party at the Great Falls carrying the delayed letters. He was euphoric.

"There is a sensation felt on receiving news after such a long silence, and in such a remote corner of the globe more easily felt then described. I am not ashamed to say (although it might be thought weakness by some) I rose from my mat four different times during the night to read my letters; in fact before morning I might say I had them by heart - my eyes never closed."

One of those eyes was now proving painful. Physically and mentally, David Douglas was increasingly paying the price for his relentless pursuit of knowledge. The inland Indian's less appealing character seemed to depress him. Smoke had revealed the bearers of his mail.

"I was delighted beyond measure to find it the camp of the brigade from the sea. I cannot describe the feeling which seizes me on seeing a person again, although I am but partially acquainted with them. After travelling in the society of savages for days together and can but speak a few words of their language, assuredly the face of a Christian although strange speaks friendship."

David travelled back up river to Walla Walla with those fine people. Seeing his state, they had given him a clean shirt and cooked him supper, food that also fed the soul. He now had an opportunity to follow further with them.

"Monday, 17th - In company with Mr. Wark and McDonald started on a journey by water with a party of twenty-eight men for the fork of Lewis and Clark's River, about 150 miles from the Columbia."

The river they paddled up was today's Snake. Their mission was to meet Indians who would sell horses. The land was barren, the heat oppressive. Travel was only possible in the cool of the morning before 10 o'clock and afternoon after 4. David decided "the only thing I might say that renders it superior to the deserts of Arabia is abundance of good water enjoyed in inland voyages. That excepted there is but little difference."

"On Monday arrived at the branches of the river at dusk, where was a camp of three different nations, upwards of five hundred men able to bear arms.....On Wednesday a conference was held and ended favourably with great splendour by dancing, singing, haranguing and smoking. all were dressed in their best garments, and on the whole presented a fine spectacle and certainly a new one to me."

Fine as was the spectacle, it did not draw David's eyes from the Blue Mountain Range, again in view and much nearer. MacDonald provided a French Canadian companion, Cock de Lard. David pushed on to climb the first peak leaving the Cock to care for the horses On top was a remarkable spring. Eleven feet in diameter, it appeared bottomless. Beside it was a thicket of no less remarkable gooseberry bushes. David had received a letter from Donald Munro, his fellow Scot and Head Gardener. He was very much with him here.

"This fine species I have not seen before; should it prove new, I hope it may be called R. Munroi, as I have called the spring Munro's Fountain; at the same time how delighted he would feel to see such in the garden."

The travellers returned to camp after an overnight ride. Cock de Lard had not packed sufficient salmon for two days away. His navigation was equally amiss, they went adrift by ten miles. Exhausted, Douglas fell into bed at sunrise. It was to be a short sleep.

"I had not been asleep more than two hours when I was hurriedly aroused to take on myself the profession of a soldier, a misunderstanding having taken place between the interpreter and one of the chiefs; the latter accusing the former of not translating faithfully, words became high till at last the poor man of language had a handful of his long jet hair torn out by the roots."

The chief concerned did not take kindly to being reproved for his boorish behaviour. He returned with his following, guns cocked, bows strung. The expedition stood to arms in defence of the unfortunate translator. Despite his humble status he was under the protection of the company. In time tension lessened, jaw jaw replaced war war.

"Many of them possessed qualifications that would be no disgrace to a modern orator. Although there is much repetition in their harangues, delivered with such vehemence and intense feeling, they are uniformly natural and are certainly calculated either to tie the knot of affection or sympathy, or rouse the mind to discord of war. I have observed speakers so overcome that they sobbed and cried aloud, and the proceedings delayed until they recovered."

When the First Nation ceased being overcome by their own verbosity, presents brought peace. Despite friendship being restored, David decided it would have been imprudent to leave the camp.

McDonald and the canoes sailed down the Snake. David decided to cross north to Fort Colville on the Columbia with Wark and the horses. Botanically it was a relatively richer trail.

At the Fort on the 16th August 1826, David Douglas became concerned to send by sea on September's ship, his gleanings of one hundred and twenty seed collections. Sixty nine papers of seeds plus two linen shirts were left for overland transmission. Many roots and Indian artefacts were packed to travel with him to the coast. The Little Wolf, a chief of the Okanagan was engaged as guide down a very fierce river. As ever, politics precluded progress. A warlike party of Cootanies arrived to dispute fishing rights.

"The parties met stark naked in our camp, painted, some red, black, white, and yellow, with their bows strung, and such as had muskets and ammunition were charged. Ward-caps of calumet-eagle feathers were the only articles of dress they had on....The whole day was spent in clamour and haranguing, and as we were not sure what might be the result we prepared for the worst."

Dease intervened personally, stunning one archer who had drawn on the opposing chief. In time he managed to sell peace to this multi-coloured mob. A great feast with accompanying uproar now ensued. The Little Wolf as one of the principals delayed leaving, eventually a substitute was found. On the 19th, David Douglas left for Fort Colville overwhelmed by the kindness of John Warren Dease.

"I left this delightful place highly gratified, having made a tolerable addition to my collection and received every kindness from the hospitable people which they had in their power to show. Being short of clothing, Mr. Dease gave me a pair of leather trousers made of deerskin and a few pairs of shoes, which in my present state are very acceptable. He provided me with three of his best horses, one for my guide, one for carrying my little articles, and one for myself."

John Wark loaned another necessity of life, his double-barrelled rifle-pistol. Alone again David descended the Columbia and arrived at Walla Walla too weak to eat. However, he had to hasten on and Black provided him with two guides to the Great Falls. At the dreaded Dalles was the inevitable congregation.

"On the Dalles were at least five hundred to six hundred persons. I learned that the chief Pawquanawaka, who would have been my last guide to the sea was not at home; but as I am now in my own province again, and understand the language tolerably well, I had no difficulty in procuring two."

David Douglas was coming home to the land he had come to love, between the Pacific Mountains and the sea. Before leaving, seventy three men came and smoked with him. One stole his tobacco box. Alone, standing on a rock, he "gave them a reprimand, calling them all the low names used to each other among themselves." He slept unmolested, bravery was recognised.

"Arrived at the village on the Grand Rapids at three and repaired to the house of Chumtalia, the chief, and my old guide last year, where I had some salmon and whortleberries laid before me on a mat."

David Douglas was home, back among the kindlier people of the great forest. He left before sunrise for the village of the Scottish chiefs.

"I had the gratification of landing safe at Fort Vancouver at midday, after traversing nearly eight hundred miles of the Columbia Valley in twelve days and unattended by a single person, my Indian guides excepted."

David's whole amazing expedition over hot hostile territory in the inland Columbia Basin was around three thousand miles. His appearance amazed the denizens of the Fort, they immediately believed him the sole survivor of a canoe wreck on the swollen river.

"I had a shirt, a pair of leather trousers, an old straw hat, neither shoe nor stocking nor handkerchief of any description, and perhaps from my careworn visage had some appearance of escaping from the gates of death."

David Douglas was a man of faith who carried a Bible through his travels and travails. In that translation brought about by King James the Sixth of Scotland and First of the United Kingdom, he would have read the words of St. Paul in his second letter to the members of the Church at Corinth. Two verses in the eleventh chapter are in the main particularly appropriate to the journey just completed.:

"In journeyings often, in perils of water....in perils by the heathen....
in perils in the wilderness.
In weariness and painfulness, in watchings often, in hunger and thirst,
in fastings often, in cold and nakedness."

CHAPTER SIX

The Saga of the Sugar Pine

David Douglas is justly commemorated in the name of Douglas Fir, foun first by Archibald Menzies. David, so respective of his predecessor in the Pacifi North West, would have welcomed the change made by the botanica establishment, when it was altered from Pseudotsuga taxifolia to Pseudotsug menziesii. Found by Menzies, introduced by Douglas, was a familiar refrain of text on trees.

The Sugar Pine, Pinus lambertiana, was found and introduced by Davi Douglas. His ambition to obtain its seed transcends all other endeavours. It wa his most focused achievement as a botanical adventurer - the term botanica traveller is too bland to apply to this story.

David had met Aylmer Bourke Lambert in England. This wealthy man wa ambitious to be the ultimate authority on pines, really conifers, as a whole. He ha produced a book and looked forward to a second edition enriched by Douglas' discoveries. Today his works are in the past. The generosity of David Douglas gav his name to a superb pine.

For the first fortnight of September 1826, David regained his strength a Fort Vancouver. He had caught the sailing of the ship Dryade and sent off hi collection to the end of August. Harvesting at home continued.

"Employed myself gleaning a few seeds of choice plants found last yea: Ribes sanguineum, Gaultheria shallon, Acer macrophyllum, Berberis acqifoliun Acer circinnatum; laid in specimens of Pinus taxifolia with fine cones, and collecte a few sections of the various woods, gums, and barks of the different timbers tha compose the forest in this neighbourhood."

At times his mind was far from the Fort. A great tree to the south ha intrigued him. For the first time he had seen seed before the tree. Just over a yea before, he had visited the village of the Calapooies and found the seeds in thei tobacco pouches. They came from great trees which grew further south.

First David enlisted the help of a trapper, Jean Batiste Desportes McKa; who operated in the area. During February 1826, he returned with one cone. I was massive, 17 inches long and at the widest, 10 inches in circumference Professor Hooker in Glasgow received a preliminary report on this potentially grea pine. David described his plan of action.

"I intend to bring home such an assemblage of specimens as will allow correct figure to be taken of this tree, and also to try my success with a bag of it seeds."

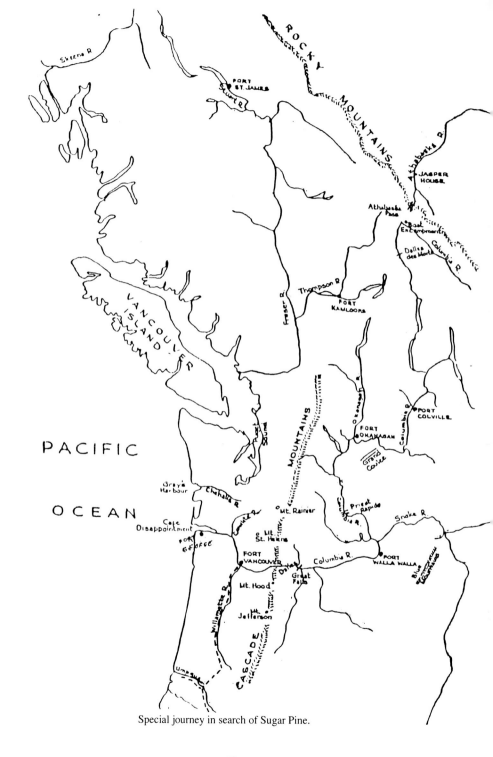

Special journey in search of Sugar Pine.

Jean Batiste was the key to a foray south up the Multnomah and further. Unfortunately, he left before David's return. However, a major expedition under Chief Trader Alexander Rodrick McLeod was to extend exploration beyond the River to the Umqua Mountains, the country of the Sugar Pine. The ever kindly Chief Factor, Dr. McLoughlan, gave his blessing to the brigade having a botanist attached. Further, he provided "one of his finest and best horses." It could be ridden or carry the botanist's basic baggage.

"Packed six quires of paper and other little articles for my business, and provided myself with a small copper kettle and a few trifles, with a little tobacco for presents and to pay my way on my return. Of personal property (except what will be on me), one strong linen and one flannel shirt; and as heavy rains may be expected, being near the coast, I will indulge myself with two blankets and my tent."

With this "indulgence" David Douglas set out on the most dangerous of all his botanical travels. He left the Fort on the 20th September 1823 in a boat with a Mr. Manson and twelve men. Two days later they caught up with the brigade. This was a rocky river, canoes were damaged. The horses proved a problem, eternally straying overnight and so delaying departure. Partly this was because the Indians had fired the land before them. Like the heather burning shepherds on the Scottish hills, they sought young vegetation. In the Indians' culture this would in time attract deer. As in Scotland, in the immediate it produced a barren land.

"Most parts of the country burned; only little patches in the valleys and on the flats near the low hills that verdure is to be seen. Some of the natives tell me it is done for the purpose of urging the deer to frequent certain parts, to feed, which they leave unburned, and of course they are more easily killed. Others say that it is done in order that they might the better find wild honey and grasshoppers, which serve as articles of winter food."

Whatever the objects of management, the Indians like the Scottish shepherds probably found that "it was easier to set the heather on fire than put it out." Deer were difficult to find in this devastated area. The brigade carried little food and required to live off the land. Their progress was initially constrained. Venison when procured was well prepared with ravishing results. David describes such a super sylvan repast.

"McKay made us some fine steaks, and roasted a shoulder of the doe for breakfast, with an infusion of Mentha borealis sweetened with a small portion of sugar. The meal laid on the clean mossy foliage of Gaultheria Shallon in lieu of a plate and our tea in a large wooden dish hewn out of the solid, and supping it from the horns of the mountain sheep or Mouton Gris of the voyageurs. A stranger can hardly imagine the hospitality and kindness shown among those people. If they have a hut, or failing that, if the day is wet, one of brushwood is made for you, and whatever they have in the way of food you are unceremoniously and seemingly with much good will invited to partake."

The people of the brigade were the normal components of the Company. Scots lead French Canadian troops. The latter may have been part Indian. Some Indians of the east crossed the Rockies in the service. Jean Batiste Desportes McKay probably had the blood of all three. His arrival certainly helped the commissariat considerably. David welcomed him for other reasons.

"At noon we were joined by Jean Batiste McKay and two Iroquois hunters on their way to the Umpqua River. McKay informs me that he had five days ago sent one of his people on to collect the cones I spoke of to him last spring, lest the season should be past before we would be there."

Travel over the burned vegetation was sore on man and beast. David described the torment in botanical terms.

"On the less fertile places, on a gravely dry bottom, where the trees are scrubby and small, a curious species of Viscum, with ovate leaves is found abundantly. I recollect Dr. Hooker asking me if I ever saw it on oak in Scotland, which I never did. As no place could be found for fodder for the horses, we had to travel till four o'clock, when we camped at a low point of land near a woody rivulet. Marched twenty-one miles. My feet tonight are very painful and my toes cut with the burned stumps of a strong species of Arundo and Spirea termentosa."

David's companions probably cursed the constraints and oblivious to Count Carol Linné's system, soldiered on. In time the burn was passed, but the further they progressed the more demanding became the route. The crossing over to the valley of the west flowing Umpqua River was laborious in the extreme. The 16th of October 1826 was one of those days.

"Passed three ridges of mountains, the highest about 2700 feet. Mr. McLeod and I took the lead and were followed by Batiste McKay and the two hunters, hewing the branches down that obstructed the horses from passing. The whole distance not so much as a hundred yards of ground at the same level, and numerous fallen trees, some of which measured 240 feet long and 8 feet in diameter - I am aware that it could hardly be credited to what a prodigious size they attain. The rain of the past two days before rendered the footing for the poor horses very bad; several fell and rolled on the hills and were arrested by trees, stumps, and brushwood. As I apprehended some accident, I thought it prudent to carry my gleanings on my back, which were tied up in a bear's skin."

The weary advance party reached the upper reaches of the Umpqua that night. The remainder did not join them until the next day, their horses were exhausted.

"The horses with my articles arrived at four o'clock in a sad condition. The tin-box containing my note-book and small papers broken and the sides pressed close together; a small canister of preserving powder in a worse state; the only shirt except the one now on my back worn by rubbing between them like a piece of surgeons lint. In the evening arranging my papers and found nothing materially injured. I am glad that I took the precaution of carrying the specimens of seeds and plants on my back otherwise they would have been much destroyed."

Now at last they were in the country of the great pine. David's route was upward into the higher hills, the brigade went down the valley of the River to the sea. McKay provided him with an Indian youth who spoke Chinook, which David had mastered, as well as the local Umpqua speech. They paid a courtesy call on the local chief, Centrenose by name. Once again Native Americans are sympathetically described by Douglas.

"The dress of the men is skins of the small deer undressed, formed into shirts and trousers, and those of the richer sort striped and ornamented with shells, principally marine, which proves our distance from the ocean to be short. The women, a petticoat of the tissue of Thuya occidentalis, made like that worn by the Chinook females, and a sort of gown of dressed leather, in form differing from the male's only be the sleeves being more open."

The pair set off alone upriver to find a necessary fording place. It proved elusive on the swollen stream, constructing a raft appeared to be the solution. David damaged his hands so badly with the hatchet that he had to send the boy down to McLeod for help.

Unwisely he went hunting alone and fell into a deep gully of deadwood, where he lay unconscious for five hours. Fate, in the form of some Calapooie Indians, was kindly. A painful chest added to the blistered hands determined the end of this first foray. Deeply disappointed he rejoined the brigade. No longer able to be in the lead he struggled away from the Sugar Pine country.

"As no one could ride through such a rough country, I was obliged to walk and but little able to endure it. Remained in the rear, and by so doing had the way well pathed for me....find myself much broken by this day's march; travelled ten miles."

Eventually they neared the sea and a coastal Indian village. Fresh fish seemed to restore the battered botanist to his usual philosophic state. The local ladies attracted his attention.

"I observe that the women are mostly all tatooed, principally the whole of the lower jaw from the ear, some in lines from ear to the mouth, some across, some spotted, some completely blue; it is done by a sharp piece of bone and a cinder from the fire. It is considered a great mark of beauty, I have little doubt that such a lady in London would make a fine figure, particularly when a little red and green earth is applied to the lower part of the face."

David Douglas was not to be distracted by those beautified belles, pines not petticoats dominated his mind. Chief Centrenose of the Calapooies came into camp on the 22nd October. Through McLeod's good graces, he agreed to give one of his sons to aid the young Scot towards the Sugar Pines. This time the local contact helped. Braves joined them to cross by canoe, no raft required. Speech alone was a problem.

"I could not utter a single syllable, but by signs they kindled my fire, brought me water, nuts, roots of Phalangium quamash, and a sort of meal made of the Syngenesious plant spoken of before."

Further fortified by this botanical breakfast, the botanist moved on over a terrain of deep gullies, rocky and obstructed by fallen timber. An almost impenetrable thicket followed this natural obstacle course. The elements seemed to conspire against him.

"Wednesday, 25. - Last night was one of the most dreadful I have ever witnessed. The rain, driven by the violence of the wind, rendered it impossible for me to keep any fire, and to add misery to my affliction my tent was blown down at midnight.

Sleep was of course not to be had, every ten or fifteen minutes immense trees falling produced a crash as if the earth was cleaved asunder, which with the thunder peal on peal before the echo of the former died away, and the lightening in zigzag and forked flashes, had on my mind a sensation more than I can ever give vent to; and more so when I think of the place and the circumstances.

My poor horses were unable to endure the violence of the storm without craving of me protection, which they did by hanging their head over me and neighing."

As the Scots saying goes - "it was no a night for man or beast to be oot in." Robert Burns's comic hero, Tam O' Shanter, sallied out in a similar one and found "the Diel had business in the land." David dried his damp clothing before setting off. He "indulged" himself with "a fume of tobacco being the only thing I could afford." He soldiered on for thirteen miles, suffering severe headaches and pain in his stomach with giddiness and dimness of sight. Some salmon, out of season, scarcely eatable, obtained from Indians, sustained him for another three miles. Refreshed by a night's sleep, his journal entry for the 26th October 1826 opens with a gem.

"When my people are made acquaint with my travels, they may think I have told them nothing but my miseries. That may be very correct, but I know that such objects as I am in quest of are not obtained without a share of labour, anxiety of mind, and sometimes risk of personal safety."

Today was to be the great day of discovery. David left at daybreak, the guide kept by the horses and the camp. Alone he would find that superb Sugar Pine.

First problem arrived within half an hour. Encountering an Indian, he found himself facing a drawn bow. Fearless himself, David believed fear motivated his potential antagonist. He laid down his gun and invited the other by signs to place his bow beside it. After this remarkable achievement without words, they sat and smoked. David drew a Sugar Pine cone. The Indian indicated that the treasure grew to the south.

"With my pencil I made a rough sketch of the cone and pine I wanted and showed him it, when he instantly pointed to the hills about fifteen to twenty miles to the south. As I wanted to go in that direction, he seemingly with much good-will went with me."

Of the many incidents in the saga of this young Scot, this one seems selected from the Bible he believed in. The picture of those two men, braves both, walking together in harmony though unable to converse for hours, friends instead of foes, is inspirational.

"At midday I reached my long-wished Pinus (called by the Umpqua tribe Natele), and lost no time in examining and endeavouring to collect specimens and seeds."

David suggests new and strange things make initially great impressions on us, and our tendency is to over-rate them. Conscious of his solitary state, far from the Fort and the brigade, his journal written at the eve of this epic day is revealing.

"Lest I should never see my friends to tell them verbally of this most beautiful and immensely large tree, I now state the dimensions of the largest one I could find that was blown down by the wind. Three feet from the ground, 57 feet 9 inches in circumference; 134 feet from the ground, 17 feet 5 inches; extreme length 215 feet."

The great trees were straight, smooth barked, and devoid of branches two thirds of their trunk. Only the largest had cones. The only way to get them down was by shooting. The botanical pursuit was to bring problems."

"The branches pendulous, and the cones hanging from their points like small sugar-loaves in a grocers shop.... I took my gun and was busy clipping them from the branches with ball when eight Indians came at the report of my gun. They were all painted with red earth, armed with bows, arrows, spears of bone, and flint knives, and seemed to me to be anything but friendly."

David was "determined to fight for life." His life's end might have been here in this grove of Sugar Pines on the Klamath Mountains of the American State of Oregon, far from Scone and Scotland.

"I perceived one string his bow and another sharpen his flint knife with a pair of wooden pincers and hang it on the wrist of the right hand, which gave me ample testimony of their inclination. To save myself I could not do by flight and without hesitation I went backward six paces and cocked my gun, and then pulled from my belt one of my pistols which I held in my left hand."

Ten minutes passed, wordless, below the pines. The leader eventually made a sign for tobacco. David indicated that it would be available in return for cones collected. Surprisingly they scattered to start collecting. Douglas fled with three cones and a few twigs. He wrote that night with some satisfaction, "all contained fine seed". They certainly had not been obtained without "labour, anxiety of mind, and sometimes risk of personal safety." His epilogue to this epic day completes the picture.

"How irksome a night is to such a one as me under my circumstances! Cannot speak a word to my guide, not a book to read, constantly expecting an attack, and the position I am now in is lying on the grass with my gun beside me, writing by light of my Columbian candle-namely, a piece of wood containing rosin."

A brush with bears followed on the morning of the 27th, rather than the return of the Indians - a minor matter which was settled easily. At twenty yards, two died and one fled. Small as the seed haul had been, David Douglas had little left in reserve to botanise on. Like Saint Paul, in some situations he has to retreat.

"With hostile Indians and incessant rains, together with the lateness of the season, fatigued and broken down I could have but little zeal to continue my exertions; and after consideration what I ought to do, I resolved to return to the sea and there wait the arrival of Mr. McLeod from the south."

On the 4th of November they met at the base camp. McLeod told him of another tree, further south by other rivers.

"The fine-smelling tree is more plentiful than on this river, that it takes the place of the pines; he measured some 12 feet round, 70 to 100 feet in length, and the lightest breath of wind to stir the leaves sends a fragrance through the whole grove."

Even this arboreal delight could not tempt David Douglas. He had to return to recuperate at his home on the Columbia. Two men were returning with nine horses to Fort Vancouver, the remainder of the brigade were moving south. It was an opportunity too good to miss. McLeod even apologies for the meagre rations for a week, all he could spare. David owed much to Alexander Roderick.

"I have made up my mind to return, and shall retain a grateful recollection of the kindness and assistance I have uniformly had from this gentleman. (Recollect on your arrival in London to get him a good rifle gun as a present)."

The return north by the Multnomah was no less rugged than the advance. River after river joining it was a challenge to cross. David completed his journey by canoe. He arrived home at eight in the evening of Sunday 19th November 1826 after an absence of two months.

"From fatigue and constant exposure to the rain and cold, my ankles, which were slightly inflamed, swelled accompanied by acute pain, and obliged me to remain within doors for nine days. Arranged what plants I had collected dried and put up seed, made a small packing-box and repaired some of my shoes."

By the 8th December, he was a "little recovered". Since time lay heavy on his hands, he had to go down to the sea again. It was time to take leave of his friend, chief Cockqua of the Chinooks.

CHAPTER SEVEN

Home By Hudson Bay

"Monday, January 1st - Morning dull but dry. The New year was ushered 1 by a discharge of the great guns at daybreak. Day spent much to my satisfaction: fter breakfast took a ride on horseback and carried my gun; returned at dusk to inner. The evening, like many I have passed in N.W. America, lay heavy on my ands."

So opens David Douglas's Journal for 1827 in marked contrast to a year efore. By his own estimate he had travelled 3932 miles over those twelve months. he sense of achievement must have been great. He had explored in Ecotopia and eyond the Cascades. A rich harvest had been reaped. Satisfied, the time had ome to return, not by the sterile ocean alone, but across the continent.

"Tuesday 20th March- showery all day. Preparations being made for the nnual express across the continent: by five o'clock in the afternoon I left Fort 'ancouver in company with Mr. Edward Ermatinger for Hudson Bay, Messrs. IcLoughlin, McLeod, Annance and Pambrun for the interior."

As the Chief Factor was with the party, the leaving lacked the usual eremonial. However, the customary stop overnight after the first hours paddling, vas given to the voyageurs. The scientific traveller exited the previous scenes of is success with the same sense of purpose as the previous year.

"Though happy of the opportunity of returning to my native land, yet I onfess I certainly left with regret a country so interesting."

I walked the whole distance from this place to Fort Colville on the Kettle 'alls, which occupied twenty-five days. Not a day passed but brought something ew in botany or zoology. The beautiful Erythronium maximum and Claytonia anceolata were in full bloom among the snow."

Zoology was part of David's remit and he discharged it by shooting and reserving specimens as assiduously as he plucked plants and selected seeds. Acquiring a live eagle was a particular prize. At Fort Colville he suffered a etback.

"The first night of my arrival, I had the great misfortune to get my pair of rouse devoured, the skins torn to pieces by the famished Indian dogs of the place. Although they were closely tied in a small oilcloth and hung from the tent poles, he dogs gnawed and ate the casing, which were leather thongs. Grieved at this eyond measure. Carried the cock bird 457, and the hen 304 miles on my back, and hen unfortunately lost them."

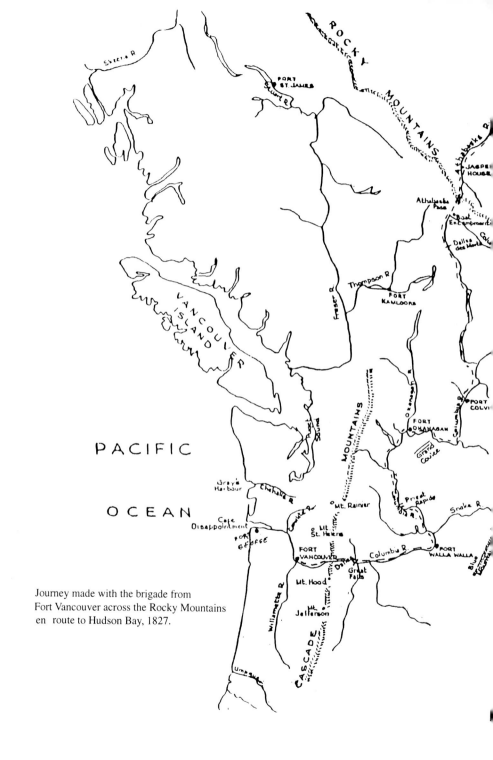

PACIFIC

OCEAN

Journey made with the brigade from
Fort Vancouver across the Rocky Mountains
en route to Hudson Bay, 1827.

Deeply disappointed, David wrote Archibald McDonald down at Fort Okanagan regarding replacements which might be sent by sea on the next ship. He also wrote Cockqua on another species reminding him of a promised specimen. Emerging from ecological utopia was not easy for one so zealous, but the time had come to depart. The 17th of April was that dreaded day.

"I in company with Mr. McLoughlin and Mr. McLeod took an airing on horseback and returned at dusk to dinner. About nine o'clock at night I was conveyed to my camp, about a mile from the establishment, where we pitched in order that no time would be lost in starting in the morning by them, who spent a few minutes with us and then returned."

When the Chief Factor and the chief Trader rode away towards Fort Colville, David Douglas must finally have felt he had left this land. Tomorrow he would turn his back on it forever and never meet them again. He might have heard in his head an old adage - a man may leave Scotland but Scotland will never leave the man. Equally, never would this lovely land leave him. Emotion must have overwhelmed.

"Having now just bid farewell to my Columbian friends, I cannot in justice to my own feelings refrain from acknowledging the kindness shown to me during my stay with them, a grateful remembrance of which I will ever cherish."

It was two o'clock in the morning of the next day before he was able to lay himself down to sleep. Not surprising, the party overslept and were not up until daybreak. They hurriedly departed lest they be seen by those who had bid them farewell. David now starts a new chapter of his travels. "My society is now confined to Mr. Eward Ermatinger, a most agreeable young man who goes to Hudson Bay with us and seven men - four Canadians and three Iroquois Indians. Our next stage is Jasper House, in the Rocky Mountains, distant about 370 miles."

The scenery was stupendous as they sailed on lakes wide enough to adequately view the unfolding panorama. The voyageurs sang their lilting French songs, the young Company clerk played the flute, David delighted in describing the scenes and deplored his inability to draw.

"Sky beautiful at sunset, the snowy summits of the hills tinted with gold; the parts secluded from his rays are clothed with cloudy branches of the pine wearing a darker hue, while the river at the base is stealing silently along in the silvery brightness or dashes through the dark recesses of a rocky Dalle. How glad should I feel if I could do justice to my pencil (when you go home, begin to learn)."

Of all David Douglas's writings this is the part where his spirit soars. Always appreciative of beauty, normally his interests in parts obscure the whole. The grandeur of the Rocky Mountains dominates all as they come to the end of their voyage. At Boat Encampment, the canoes were cached to await the coming of the west-bound brigade. They had passed the gloomy Dalles des Morts, the

Narrows of Death, where a previous party had perished. The inland rain forest was less lofty than the coast and denser. The Rockies were overbearingly close at hand.

"Passed this place as the sun was tipping the mountains and his feeble rays now and then seen through the shady forests, imparts a melancholy sensation of no ordinary description, filling the mind with awe on beholding this picture of gloomy wildness....."

".........Although I have been travelling for the last fifteen days surrounded by high snow mountains, and the eye has become familiar to them and apt to lose the exalted idea of their magnitude, yet on beholding those mentioned impressed on the mind a feeling beyond what I can express. I would say a feeling of horror."

Struggling in snow shoes they climbed in increasing depths of snow up a narrowing pass. The river running through required to be forded more as the sides of the pass became steeper, no less than fourteen times on one day. The last lap proved to be the worst. David was almost defeated.

"The ravines and gullies unmeasurable, and towards noon becoming soft sinking, ascending two steps and sometimes sliding back three, the snowshoe twisting and throwing the weary traveller down (and I speak as I feel) so feeble that lie I must among the snow, like a broken-down waggon-horse entangled in his harnessing, weltering to rescue myself. Obliged to camp at noon, two miles up the hill, all being weary. No water; melted snow which makes good tea; find no fault with the food."

The load this weary human horse carried was minimal, yet in those conditions so big a burden. At an overnight stop, the journal tells of its content.

"Examined the seeds in my tin box and found them in good order repacked them without delay and at the same time tied up all my wardrobe, toilet &c., which is as follows: four shirts (two linen and two flannel), three handkerchiefs, two pairs stockings, a drab cloth jacket, vest and trousers of the same, one pair tartan trousers, vest and coat; bedding, one blanket; seven pairs of deerskin shoes, or as they are called, moccasins; one razor, soap-box, brush, strop and one towel, with half a cake of Windsor soap.

In addition to these I was presented with a pair of leggings by Mr Ermatinger, made out of the sleeves of an old blanket-coat or capot of the voyageurs. This, trifling as it may appear, I esteem in my present circumstances as very valuable. When the half of this my sole property is on back, the remainder is tied in a handkerchief of the common sort."

May 1st was a special day in Old Scotland. People with their cattle migrated up to the highest pastures. Boys reached the tops of the Bens. This was eltane, when great fires blazed in a ceremony harking back to the days of the Druids.

This day in 1827, the little party finally reached the top of the Athbasca ass. They had toiled up the last steepest, snowiest ascent from daybreak to midday where they camped exhausted. After they had rested and breakfasted, one our later David Douglas made the Beltane climb of his boyhood, to the top of the nearest peak. As in his youth in Perthshire, thoughts of the Druids were replaced y that of the Creator God brought by the Celtic Church to his native land.

"The labour of ascending the lower part, which is covered with pines, is reat beyond description, sinking on many occasions to the middle. Half way up he vegetation ceases entirely, not so much as a vestige of moss or lichen on the tones. Here I found it less laborious as I walked on the hard crust. One-third from he summit it becomes a mountain of pure ice, sealed for ever by Nature's hand as a momentous work of Nature's God....

Nothing as far as the eye could perceive, but mountains such as I was on, nd many higher, some rugged beyond any description, striking the mind with orror blended with a sense of the wondrous works of the Almighty."

David Douglas delighted in honouring others by bestowing their name to is scientific discoveries. He now had another first to record, the first ascent of hose northerly Rockies. The peak of his progression was to honour, "R. Brown Esq., the illustrious botanist, no less distinguished by the amicable qualities of his efined mind. " He looked south and saw a peak, perfect, sharp to the point. One man alone was worthy to have such an everlasting monument.

"I named Mount Hooker, in honour of my early patron the enlightened and earned Professor of Botany at the University of Glasgow, Dr. Hooker, whose kindness I, in a great measure owe my success in life, and I feel exceedingly glad of an opportunity of recording a simple but sincere token of my kindest regard for im and respect for his profound talents."

That first day of May 1827 saw another famous man honoured by a less angible memorial, one which in normal circumstances would be destined to decay. However, over one hundred and seventy years later, the first named Franklin's Grouse may be seen at the National Museum of Scotland in Edinburgh. It was aved from supper and preserved for posterity by David Douglas in the Athabasca Pass.

The ultimate symbol of the travellers having reached the mid way mark of heir journey across the Continent, was a little lake. Governor George Simpson, was to name it, the Committee's Punch Bowl, in honour of the executive committee of the Hudson Bay Company.

They followed the flow east, descending rapidly down steeper terrain then the west. Snow stopped sooner, there was even a person out looking for them Jacques Cardinal, with eight horses.

"The difference of climate and of soil, and the amazing difference of the variety and seize of the vegetation, are truly astonishing; one would suppose one was in another hemisphere, the change is so sudden and so great."

On the 4th of May the mountain portage was over. Embarking at daybreak in two birch bark canoes, the flow brought them to Jasper House at two o'clock. To use David's words, this outpost consisted of "three small hovels on the left side of the river." Today's town offers much superior accommodation to travellers However, the hovels were to have a ceilidh that night. Voyageurs gave vent to their feelings of relief. those simple servants of the Company had a spirit not long depressed.

"An old violin was found at our new lodgings, and Mr. E.'s servant being something of a performer nothing less than dancing in the evening would suit them which they kept up for a few hours. This may show how little they look on hardship when passed; only a few days ago, and they were as much depressed as they are now elated."

On the 6th, the brigade set off sailing down river to Fort Assiniboine. Soon another party was overtaken, fellow sufferers from across the Rockies. George McDougall and his four followers had come from Fort St. James on Stuart Lake This most northern outpost of New Caledonia was egressed by the upper Fraser River, a terrible trial. The Fort, when reached, was not happy to receive such a party.

"Tuesday, 8th - Provisions being scarce and from the hostile disposition of the Indian tribes in the south, it was deemed unsafe to go in such a small party, we intended to wait for the people from Lesser Slave Lake who are hourly expected As Mr. McDougall was going down the river with the intention of procuring food for the men from Columbia and Western Caledonia, I accepted an invitation merely to see the country, being yet too early for affording me any plants, and by doing this I may put myself in possession of some birds."

By birch bark canoe, eleven left to find food. Over forty seven miles of river they found nothing. Then a chance encounter with a Nipissing hunter resulted in a hearty meal of half-dried beaver-meat. Restored, they followed on to where the river from Lesser Slave Lake meets the Athabasca. There they met a party from the Lake headed by John Stuart, Chief Factor of the district, who received David Douglas "in the most kindly manner". A Scot, from Strathspey Stuart had joined the North West Company and was with Fraser on the Fraser River expedition. His name is commemorated in Stuart Lake.

"Mr. Stuart, I find to have a more intimate knowledge of the country than any person I have yet seen, and a good idea of plants and other departments in natural history. He was the first individual who crossed the Rocky Mountains and established Western New Caledonia in 1805, and the same year reached the Pacific at Fraser's River near Puget Sound, and has since been over a vast extent of country in those parts, first explored by Sir A. McKenzie. He has been also on the Columbia."

David could not have met a better man in this new and different side of the Continent. Douglas developed his future plans on the Chief Factor's advice. He was also indebted to him for the provision of two horses. Stuart also had information on the Franklin Expedition, which had now returned south.

Two naturalists from Scotland were with it. Dr., later Sir John Richardson, was a native of Dumfries and a medical graduate of Edinburgh University. Thomas Drummond from Forfar bore a great Perthshire name and came from adjacent Angus. David longed to meet them.

Drummond had not gone north with the main party but botanised along the Athabasca. There he had fallen in with Finan McDonald whom David had entrusted with a precious box of seed. He gave the box to Drummond to await Douglas's arrival. David Douglas, like the future Queen Victoria, was not amused. For the first time a note of professional jealousy enters his journal.

"Learned that Mr. McDonald, the person who had in charge my box of seeds addressed to be left at Fort Edmonton on the Saskatchewan River, had endured much misery descending the Athbasca, the ice being taken before he made good half his journey. In company with him Mr. Drummond. Hope my box is safe do not relish botanist coming in contact with another's gleanings)."

David dispatched to Edmonton with haste. The country was one of bogs, swamps, and mires, with rivers to cross. It had nothing to distract him.

"This uninteresting wretched country afforded me no plants.....breakfasted in a low wet plain near a narrow lake.....passed a deep muddy swamp a mile broad.....all the hollow parts of the plains overflowed with water.

Being then only nine miles from Fort Edmonton on the Saskatchewan, my spirits revived and I hastily tripped over the ground and passed many muddy creeks and shallow sheets of water, wading to the middle."

He had started with a brigade but felt he must push on before them on land. He even felt he would be fleeter without a horse, the motivation was in his mind. "I am most anxious to learn the fate of my packet of seeds." On the 21st of May, night falling, losing sight of the landscape, he suddenly found the Fort.

"I heard the evening howl of the sledge-dogs, which to me was sweet music, and perceived fires in some lodges which I knew to be near the establishment.

Being all over with mud, I returned half a mile to a small lake, stripped and plunged myself in and then comforted myself with a clean shirt which I carried on my back in a bundle.

He found Finan McDonald here and learned that his seed box had been damaged. Drummond had changed the papers. Exhaustion prevented further investigation that day.

"Tuesday, 22nd - Fatigued so much with yesterday's walking that no sleep could be had; rose at daybreak and had my box opened; found the seeds in much better order than could be expected from the trouble the person had before he reached this place. Only eighteen papers had suffered, amongst which I am exceedingly sorry is Paeonia. This is one of the finest plants in the collection. It often happens that the best goes first."

Satisfied his seeds were overall safe and sound, David deployed in this botanically barren country. Fauna, especially birds interested him. Perhaps he felt that this aspect of his harvesting had been under-represented. Coming closer to the coast and having horses would help transport. Specimens he shot around the fort. More interesting was a present of a live bird.

"A fine young Calumet Eagle, two years old, sex unknown, I had of Mr Rowand; brought from the Cootanie lands situation in the bosom of the Rocky Mountains near the headwaters of the Saskatchewan River. His plumage is much destroyed by the boys, who had deprived him of those in the tail that are just coming to their true colour."

Teasing him as well as plucking his feathers, had not improved the eagle's temper. David caged him with difficulty when the time came to depart. Stuart had suggested that he sail with him to Fort Carlton. Before leaving, another ceilidh was called for. This time David could not duck participation.

"No time was lost in forming a dance; and as I was given to understand it was principally on my account, I could not do less than endeavour to please by jumping, for dance I could not."

Indians were reputed to join those jollification's. The scene must have been worthy of an artist's brush.

"Around Edmonton the country is woodless and uninteresting. Embarked in Mr. Stuart's boat, in company of others, to Fort Carlton House....The scenery in this river is varied and highly picturesque."

Despite the better vegetation, botanising was still limited. On this slower stream, they slept in the canoes sailing on through the night. Food forced them to stop. They were now in the country where the antelope and buffalo played. The Pronghorns proved to be susceptible to bright colours. Wearing a red or white shirt, the hunters stalked them on all fours. The buffalo brought bigger challenge as old Finan found to his cost.

"On one of the hunting excursions Mr. F. McDonald was dreadfully lacerated by a wounded buffalo bull in the back part of his left thigh, had some rib broken, his left wrist dislocated, and was otherwise severely bruised.

Those animals have a disposition not to destroy life at once, but delight to torture. On first striking the object of their revenge, if he is stunned or feigns to be dead there is some chance of his escape; the animal in the meantime will lie down beside his victim, keeping a steadfast eye on him and the moment there is the least motion up he gets and gives another blow."

Finan had closed too soon on an animal less disabled than anticipated. It tossed him six times. Awaiting the seventh strike he "laid hold of his wig (his own words) and hung on; man and bull sank the same instant."

The other hunters were out of ammunition and had the melancholy task of standing by and watching their fellow expire. When reinforcements arrived, the problem was how to shoot the bull without injuring its victim. while tactics were being debated an excited Indian accidentally discharged his gun in the air. This had the unexpected good fortune to raise the bull, first sniffing his victim, turning him gently over, and walking off."

Now rose Doctor David to the rescue. "My lancet being always in my pocket like a watch, I had him bled and his wounds bound up, when he was carried to the boat: gave twenty-five drops of laudanum and procured sleep."

Two days later they were at Carlton, but Finan had to be forwarded to Fort Cumberland where Dr. Richardson was to be found. The tough old trader recovered, whether as a result of David's first aid or the real Doctor's professional ministrations. He retired from his Columbia travels, but returned not to his native Scotland. Canada claimed him as one of its heroes.

Douglas and Drummond met at Fort Carlton. David diplomatically describes Drummond's collection as "princely". They visited several habitats contiguous to the Fort. Further afield was unsafe as four weeks before, four miles out, the Stone Indians had murdered a voyageur. David continued downriver to Cumberland.

"Arrived at Cumberland at 5 P.M. on Saturday and was kindly welcomed by Mr. J. Leith. here I was greeted by Dr. Richardson, save from his second hazardous journey from the shores of the Polar Sea....The doctor has a splendid herbarium and a super collection in every department of natural history."

Once again the road was east towards the coast, to Norway House at the outlet of Lake Winnipeg. Here he met a former friend, John McLeod, who had carried his mail across from the Columbia. J. G. McTavish of York Factory on the coast offered him any help required. This was the North West company leader who had attacked Astor's Fort at the mouth of the Columbia, a powerful person.

Here also, David Douglas met the most powerful person of all. George Simpson (later to be knighted) was born by Loch Broom in Wester Ross. Many names were given to him, most uncomplimentary. He was the Governor on the ground of the Hudson Bay Company, a tough business man whose energetic personality and ruthless rule held the great trading empire together. Few found pleasure in meeting him.

"June 17th - This morning at daylight George Simpson, Esq., (Governor arrived from Montreal, who I state with pleasure gave sufficient testimony of hi friendly attentions and kind offices. Seeing me perhaps rather indifferentl clothed, he offered me some linen, &c., which I refused, at the same time indebte to him."

The contrast between the two Scots far from home must have been tota The great Governor in all his glory of power almost without limitation; the ragge plant-hunter prepared to work for his keep only, to advance his science.

David Douglas was now only two months away from leaving this land an within days of reaching Hudson Bay. Botany was possible, but the harvest poor o the deader lands of the Canadian Shield. South of him was long, large Lak Winnipeg. Flowing north into it was the Red River, new country. Perhaps mo: interesting of all was Lord Selkirk's settlement. How often must David have hear of this interesting place and its turbulent history. Many times it merits mention i his journal as a place to visit. Now he had the time, he waited for the opportunit; Unexpectedly it came at Norway House.

"A few days were spent here, when Captain Sir John Franklin arrived, wh politely offered me a passage in his canoe through the lake as far as the mouth (Winnipeg River on my way to Red River, which was gladly embraced."

The party left on the second of July 1827. David was given charge of packet of letters for the Red River Settlement and a box containing churc ornaments for the Roman Catholic bishop. His collections were left behin(including the wildlife.

"Sent the Calumet eagle to Hudson's Bay by a Mr. Ross, wild fowl an other meat being scarce, and as he will not eat fish I was unable to keep him at th latter place. Placed the white-headed one under the care of a woman attached t the establishment, until my return."

David Douglas set off along Lake Winnipeg on his last expeditio motivated mainly to see the Settlement. There is a plaque on a wall in the town (Kirkcudbright in the South West of Scotland. Placed there by the Provinci; Government of Manitoba, it honours the Earl of Selkirk whose settlement was th genesis of the present city of Winnipeg. This philanthropic young nobleman, major shareholder in the Hudson Bay Company, founded it as a home fc Highlanders dispossessed from their glens to provide pasture for sheep. He sold h own land to help finance the project before consumption claimed him at an ear' age. Violent attempts were made to suppress it by the North West Company usir their Metis (part Indian), providers of Pemmican from this prairie. The settleme survived Selkirk's early death. The union of the Hudson Bay Company and th

orth Westers ended this Scottish Civil War. On the 12th July it received its
isitor, parted from the party two days before.

"At sunrise passed several thinly planted low houses, with small herds of
attle wandering from the folds: humble and peasant-like these may appear too
any, to me 'who have been no sharer of civilised society for considerable time
assed' they impart a pleasant sensation....

Strangers in this quarter appear to be few: scarcely a house I passed
ithout an invitation to enter, more particularly from the Scottish settlers, who no
oubt judging by my coat (being clothed in the Stewart or Royal tartan) imagined
e a son from the bleak dreary mountains of Scotland, and had many questions to
ut to me regarding the country, which now they only see through ideal
ecollection. Appear to live comfortably and have the means of subsistence by
ttle exertion."

That last sentence is so revealing and comforting. Those poor people had
egun life in a similar settlement in Sutherland. Burned out their houses by the
gents of an alien Earl, they were separated from the land of their ancestors.
Mountains divided them and the waste of seas," to quote the Canadian Boat Song,
yet their heart remained Highland". Thanks to a Scottish Earl whose lands were
ar to the south, they survived to end their days in similar circumstances in this new
cotland.

Fort Garry was further upriver, the centre of the expanding settlement.
he Roman Catholic Mission was here. David bore ornaments for the Bishop,
onseigneur J. N. Provenchier. He was "much delighted with the meek, dignified
ppearance of the Bishop....a man of the most profound acquirements, seen only
rough the thick rut of his great modesty." The other Catholic clergy were equally
npressive, as was their overall mission to the Indians.

On Sunday, David arrived at the English Church, half an hour late, having
ken the wrong path. The Reverend David Jones, seeing him from the window, set
boy to guide him.

"This struck me as the man of the world who, in the parable, was
ompelled to go to the feast by the person stationed on the wayside. After the
ervice Mr. Jones received me with every kindness, and politely invited me to his
ouse and said that I should be no stranger during my stay."

David Douglas enjoyed the simple faith of the old Kirk, which cared for the
ajority of the people of Scotland. He could transcend denominations and relate
 those of other persuasions, in common Christianity. David delighted always in
e company of his fellow Scots in this vast Continent.

"Called at Fort Garry and presented myself to Donald McKenzie Esq., the
overnor of the Colony, who received me with great kindness. While a basin of tea
as preparing at my request, a large tureen of milk was placed on the table which I
und excellent. I handed Governor Simpson's note, but found the note was

unnecessary with Mr. McKenzie. His conversation to me is the most acceptable from the intimate knowledge he possesses of the country west of the Rocky Mountains. In 1819 he ascended the Missouri River and crossed the Continent to the mouth of the Columbia with an American party.......He was travelled largely through the country south of the Columbia, in the interior, behind the Spanish settlements, and like all who share in such undertakings, shared in the fatigues and hardships attendant on those expeditions. But his was more than usual, being the first who ventured on those untrodden wilds."

How happy were David's days on Red River. He spoke with an Indian boy at the Mission, Spokane Garry, whose people he had met across the Rockies. He rode with one of the priests across the plains. This idyll ended on the 10th of July, McKenzie was sending a boat north up Lake Winnipeg, David had to leave to guarantee catching the ship at Hudson Bay.

"I thought it prudent to make my stay no longer. The Reverend Mr. Jones and the Reverend Mr. Cockran called on me and handed me some small packages for Hudson's Bay and England. Both these gentlemen have shown me much civility (A few seeds from the Society would be of great benefit to the missionary establishment and would be greatly received). To D. McKenzie (The Governor of the Colony) I am greatly indebted for his polite attentions. After bidding him and the Bishop adieu, I left the establishment with Mr. Hamlyn, the Surgeon for Hudson's Bay."

David Douglas's last journey would not have been normal without trouble. Winds swept over Winnipeg Lake. Like Saint Paul before Malta they were sore buffeted.

"It became boisterous and much hard labour before we got to the shore. The oars were long, and by the heavy swell it was nothing but plunging. Landed in a low thinly wooded island at half past five; our poor men exhausted, and myself somewhat anxious.....

Sunday the 12th - Last night the wind increased to a perfect hurricane and the water rose so high as to overflow our camp; so we had to betake ourselves to the boat for the night."

Two days later they were washed onto another shore, almost shipwrecked. David's words are almost Pauline, but in the midst of the storm the botanist triumphs and finds another treasure.

"Ere all the baggage was out, the waves were breaking on the shore with all the violence of a sea hurricane....

Wednesday, 15th - Weather same throughout the night; morning clear and somewhat more moderate at ten, but still unable to proceed. Found and laid in specimens of Linnaea borealis (in fruit). This is the first time I have ever seen this plant in this state. Is rare. Mr. Scouler informed me that he found it in 1825, in erfect fruit, in the shady forests of Nootka Sound: here around my tent, in sand hat has been thrown on the shore by the lake storms, in partially shaded ituations."

Flowing down river to the sea remained no less exciting.

"At noon, while descending a rapid, the boat struck heavily on the rock ind shattered seven of the timbers and planking. Just had time to reach a small sland when she filled. My hands tied up - could not get off. Dried papers: planted n a small box Erythronium grandiflorum, Lilium pudicum, and Claytonia anceolata, which I am glad are all fresh. (Why did you not bring Gaultheria alive - icross the continent - 2900 miles? It could be done)."

So wrote one who had crossed and conquered botanically the Continent of North America at its wildest. His last journal entry of the 28th of August 1827, is in keeping.

"Entered 'Steel River', a stream of some magnitude but not so rapid as the ast. Breakfasted at its junction with York River. Continued until dusk when we out to shore, boiled the kettle, and embarked under sail. Aurora borealis beautiful.

At sunrise on Tuesday I had the pleasing scene of beholding York Factory wo miles distant, the sun glittering on the roofs of the house (being covered with in) and in the bay riding at anchor the company's ship.....

The hearty welcome I had on shores of the Atlantic from Mr. McTavish and ill others was to me not a little gratifying. In the most polite manner everything :hat could add to my comfort was instantly handed; and I adduce no further proof of this gentleman's goodness than to state he had, without my knowledge made for ne a new suit of clothing, linen, &c., ready to put on......Regret the death of my Calumet Eagle; was strangled a few days ago with the cord of which he was tied by the leg: fell over the casing of one of the houses and was found dead in the morning. What can give one more pain? This animal I carried 2000 miles and now lost him, I might say, at home.

Had a note from Governor Simpson. Met Captain Black, Lieutenant Kendall, and Mr. Drummond, who arrived here yesterday.

It now only remains to state that I have had great assistance, civility, and friendly attentions from the various persons I have formed an acquaintance with during my stay in North America."

CHAPTER EIGHT

Westward Again

"In Botany my expectations have not been realised, but at the same time being in possession of several not included in the American Flora, many interesting and but partially known species, with some additional knowledge as to the geographical range of plants, an inquiry of the greatest importance, I have no reason to regret the journey. At all events, my humble exertions will I trust convey and enthuse, and draw attention to the beautifully varied verdure of N.W America."

David Douglas had kept in touch with the eminent Governor of New York State, De Witt Clinton, since his return from his expedition in that part of America. The portion of a letter written before David left from Hudson Bay is revealing. Allowing for his usual modesty it suggests a task unfinished. He had not been south to California or north to New Caledonia. There would surely be a follow on.

In London, the Horticultural Society was satiated with the seeds sent from the Columbia. They had no further plans for David Douglas. The savants of society heard his report. Honours were bestowed but in time he became dispensable.

Disappointed, David returned to Scotland. In Glasgow the Botanic Garden was flourishing under Professor Hooker's wise oversight. The sons of the second city of the empire sent home plants from afar. Douglas was delighted to find that everything was going to Glasgow, Dr. Hooker was getting all.

New books were envisaged, which would use his knowledge: Professor Hooker's own Flora Boreali-Americana, Dr. John Richardon's Fauna Boreali Americana, James Wilson's Illustrations of Zoology.

David Douglas had a destiny linked to the west of the North American Continent. Discussions between diplomats of the United States and the United Kingdom were taking place in the summer of 1828. Both had ended their war over boundaries by the Treaty of Ghent in 1814. The 49th parallel of latitude was agreed as the boundary to the summit of the Rocky Mountains. West of that was left open for further consideration. The conference was suspended during 1829 to allow for further consideration.

David Douglas had contributed to the conference by writing a memoir at the request of the Colonial Office. His opinion probably strengthened the British position. That position would be even stronger if they had a map on the table with accurate measurements to confront the Americans in the future.

Suddenly the Society found that they wanted to send David Douglas back with a remit from California to New Caledonia. This time he would be more of a Scientific Traveller, one equipped and proficient in the use of the latest scientific instruments of land measurement. David's destiny was decided, he sailed October 31st 1829.

Scone and Scotland were visited before he left. His father had died during he first expedition, he took leave of a widowed mother. He must have again met his first employer, the Mansfield Family. He was to write to the Palace about his plans during 1828 and 29. From Scotland came two new assets. He had a large Bible with bold clear print as sold in Glasgow. His eye trouble going back to his struggles in the snows during 1826, was permanent. For company and perhaps help, he brought Billy, a Scots Terrier. The muckle book and the wee dog were to be his companions to his life's end.

David Douglas returned to the Columbia River Region during June 1830, over three years after he left it. He arrived with enhanced status and was immediately accorded a personal servant. This time not a voyageur but a fellow Scot. Like so many others, William Johnstone was of the old North West Company.

David followed old trails above and below the Cascade Mountains through summer into autumn. His lost journal deprives us of the great detail of 1825-27. Fever fell on his beloved land decimating the First People. He fled this calamity on the Columbia for California.

Douglas reached this new land late in December 1830. Imperial Spain had moved north from Mexico in 1767. Their agents were not secular but clerical. From San Diego to San Francisco stretched a long line of mission stations. The Fathers cultivated the land and converted the Indians. They came direct from Mother Spain to serve selflessly. This had been a province and preserve of the Church.

When David landed at the capital, Monterey, the flag of the Mexican Republic flew over the Governor's residence. Changed times brought trouble to this paradise. Secular settlement had started. Many were Mexican and of mixed race. They felt ignored by the Fathers whose prosperity they envied. The Governor expected trouble.

At this time of tension, the arrival of a traveller was not welcome. A passport to proceed further was necessary and not obtainable. However, April 1831 saw a passport being granted to "Don David Douglas, Esquire, a British subject and a native of Scotland", (in Spanish.) The young Scot studied Spanish and backed by Latin set off to fraternise with the Fathers.

The trading forts of the Hudson Bay Company had their equivalents in the mission stations of the Holy Catholic Church. They welcomed David as a man of learning with respect. The feeling was mutual, he wrote well of them in his letters to Glasgow. Through their hospitality he crossed California. Pines and flowers he found, and saw the great Sequoia sempervirens, the Redwoods described by Archibald Menzies. Pinus coulteri commemorates a fellow botanist, Thomas Coulter, who came to California during this period.

The long predicted storm broke early in 1832. Both botanists were deflected from their duties to become reluctant soldiers. When the crises past,

Coulter set off for Colorado and David decided to return to the Columbia. He reached the River by the middle of October. As with his previous journeys he came by Honolulu, a place with a British diplomatic presence.

David Douglas had served many masters and served them well. However he had that independence of spirit and intellect which is the soul of a Scot. To the Horticultural Society of London, Douglas's decision to resign from the service would be inexplicable. David had long outgrown the Society as his letters to Glasgow testify. He had halved his seed between London and Glasgow, now all would go to Glasgow. Now he was a poor man whose salary would be sequestered to cover his costs, but he had a great personal plan. California had been covered in the south, now he was for New Caledonia in the north, and beyond.

During that sad summer of limbo in London, David Douglas first met the Russians. They were members of an expedition travelling home and had much to discuss. Together a plan was hatched that David would some day travel back botanising, from America through Siberia to Europe. The Czar was a man of Science, they would put the plan to him. Professor Hooker was party to the plan. The Director of the Imperial Botanic Garden, Dr. Fischer, was a friend and another of the Professor's pupils, John Goldie, was collecting for the Garden. Once again the Douglas-Hooker partnership was in action. Before he left California, David received a letter in French, from Baron Wrangel, Governor of the Russian Territories in America. It translates as follows -

"I learn with great joy your intention to make a journey to our region. Feel sure, Sir, that no visit has been more pleasing to me, and that open arms will be extended to you at Sitka. If you intend to return to Europe by Siberia, I can assure you in May of next year, you can carry on comfortably in one of our naval vessels to Okotsk, where the news I have heard is that a hearty welcome is prepared for you."

In the Spring of 1833, David Douglas set out for Fort St. James on Stuart Lake, the most northerly post of New Caledonia. From there he would find his way to the sea and up to Sitka in Alaska. His hopes were high as he embarked on this incredible undertaking. He could have sailed up the coast in a Russian ship, but that would have missed out territory, not a botanist's way. He was too professional to leave his work, and it was his work, in this land unfinished. In a letter to Glasgow to a young Hooker, he hopes that they will have a jaunt to the Highlands during 1835.

David reached Fort St. James during June 1833. Like Fort Vancouver on the Columbia, it too has been faithfully reconstructed. Unlike it, no modern metropolis surrounds this smaller station. It dominates a hamlet and has an aura of authenticity. It seems to be still in service. Here the devotee of David Douglas can sense his sadness looking across Stuart Lake. Today this is still a dead end, in the dull boreal forest. Here he aborted his last great adventure. However, heavy his heart, he was too tired to travel on.

They set off south, Johnston, David, and the dog Billy, by canoe down the turbulent Fraser River. Rapids wrecked their frail craft and for an eternity they spun downstream. Miraculously, all three survived. Everything was lost, including the journal which would have told this tale so well. Refurbished, they left Caledonia for Columbia. David Douglas returned to Fort Vancouver exhausted mentally and physically, fever followed. He left forever in a ship to Honolulu, where he hoped to find a passage home. It was May 1834 before he wrote to Glasgow, his first letter in over a year.

CHAPTER NINE

Right on to the End of the Road

"We steered southward for the Sandwich Islands. The island of Mauai was indistinctly seen, at sunset, of the 21st of December, 1833, forty-two miles off; and, on the 22nd, Woahu lay ten miles due west of us.

Having quitted the Harbour of Fair Haven, in Woahu, on Friday, the 27th, in an American schooner of sixty tons, she proved too light for the boisterous winds and heavy seas of those channels, and we were accordingly obliged to drop anchor in Rahaina Roads, for the purpose of procuring more ballast.....

On Tuesday, the 31st of December, we stood in for the island of Hawaii, and saw Mouna Kuah very clearly, a few small strips of snow lying only near its summit."

David Douglas was again keeping a journal, which was sent to his brother John. Once again his old self appears. Hawaii healed him initially, but his energy output soon exhausted his diminished resource. It was not possible for him to hole up in Honolulu awaiting the ship that would start him on the road home to Scotland and Scone. The hills of Hawaii lay nearer than the hills of home. Mauna Kea, Kilauea, and Mauna Loa, all stood over 13,000 feet above the sea he sailed on. Active volcanoes were to be a new phenomenon.

"My object being to ascent Mouna Kuah, as soon as possible, I started on the 7th of January, 1834, and after passing for rather more than three miles over plain country, commenced the ascent, which was however gradual, by entering the wood. Here the scenery was truly beautiful. Large timber trees were covered with creepers and species of Tillandsia, while the tree ferns gave a peculiar character to the whole country."

David Douglas, determined as ever, was back to botany again. Difficulties were no different, rain fell relentlessly.

"We continued our way under such heavy rain, as , with the already bad state of the path, rendered walking very difficult and laborious: in the chinks of the lava, the mud was so wet we repeatedly sunk in it, above our knees.....The large Tree Ferns, and other trees that shadowed it, proved no protection from the incessant rain, and I was drenched to the skin the whole day, besides repeatedly slipping into deep holes full of soft mud."

An overnight stop, spent in a small hut, with no dry fuel for a fire, broke the ascent. David's followers were not over energetic. Happiness for him was hurrying on to the top. Feeling fatigued, carrying 60 pounds of equipment, he left them behind joining two white hunters. At their mountain bothy, a fire was lit, a haven of delight wanting one amenity as David dried himself.

"Here a large fire dried my clothes, and I got something to eat, though, unluckily, my guides all lingered behind, and those who carried my blanket and tea-kettle were the last to make their appearance. Those people have no thought or consideration for the morrow; but sit down to their food, smoke and tell stories, and make themselves perfectly happy."

His happy Hawaiians must have been ever happier on the following day, the hunters shot and presented the party with the carcass of a young bull. This was their quarry.

"According to report, the grassy flanks of the mountain abound with wild cattle, the offspring of the stock left here by Capt., Vancouver, and which now prove a very great benefit to this island."

On the morning of the 12th January, the scientist reached the summit of the highest volcano on Hawaii. Nothing had prepared him for this new trial. Pain from the hot ground seared his feet, skins peeled from his face, his head ached, and his eyes became bloodshot with stiffness in their lids. Those physical problems were pinpricks to one whose spirit soared.

"Were the traveller permitted to express the emotions he feels when placed on such an astonishing part of the earth's surface, cold indeed must his heart be to the great operations of Nature, and still colder towards Nature's God, by whose wisdom and power such wonderful scenes were created, if he could behold them without deep humility and reverential awe.

Man feels himself as nothing - as if standing on the verge of another world. The death-like stillness of the place, not an animal nor an insect to be seen - far removed from the din and bustle of the world, impresses on his mind with double force the extreme helplessness of his condition, an object of pity and compassion, utterly unworthy to stand in the presence of a great and good, and wise and holy God, and to contemplate the diversified works of His hands."

Did David Douglas, worn and weary, feel that his time would not be long in this earthly paradise, before he met his maker? Celtic consciousness of the beauty of land and sea compliments the searching of the soul. Destiny decrees the part played on this stage, the earth.

Descending Mauna Kea was no less traumatic. Rain fell, rivulets ran, and "rushed in foam through the deep glens." soft underfoot, they repeatedly sunk to their knees. Lumps of lava, roots of trees, supported them as they struggled down. It hardly seemed a suitable time to botanise, as usual David did. Fifty fern species were collected and bundled.

"Spite of all the disadvantages and fatigue I underwent, still the magnificence of the scenery commanded my frequent attention, and I repeatedly sat down, in the course of the day, under some huge spreading Tree-Fern, which more resembled an individual of the Pine than the Fern tribe, and contemplated with delight the endless variety of form and structure that adorned the objects around me

On the higher part of the mountain, I gathered a Fern identical with the Asplenium viride of my own native country, a circumstance which gave me inexpressible pleasure, and recalled to my mind many of the happiest scenes of my early life."

Ferns still flourish on Kinnoul Hill, the mount of his childhood. This was the place of wonder of his early years, his Spring. Fifty fern species he found and collected in this his Fall.

Back at base, David paid his porters, part in money part in goods. They numbered sixteen in all. Five carried the botanist's baggage, eleven were required to carry the food.

"Nor was this unreasonable, for the quantity of Poe which a native will consume in a week, nearly equals his own weight! Still, though the sixteen people ate two bullocks in a week, besides what they carried, a threatened scarcity of food compelled me to return sooner than I should have done, in order that the Calabashes might be replenished.

No people in the world can cram themselves to such a degree as the Sandwich Islanders; their food is, however, of a very light kind, and easy of digestion."

Sandwiches would not have suited the natives of those islands, which carried at that time, the name of the Earl of Sandwich. The noble Lord, was one busy serving the state, some say concentrated at cards. Whatever, bread and a filling between, sufficed to fortify him for business or pleasure.

Despite those difficult logistics, David Douglas was not to be delayed. This time his object was the great volcanic crater, Kilauea, followed by Mauna Loa. They left the bay, by Hilo, and crossed a cultivated plain. Groves of bread-fruit, ponds of fish, little plantations of vegetables, surrounded dwellings. His followers fascinated him enough to again comment on their constant need to be fuelled with food.

"As usual there was a formidable display of luggage, consisting of Tapas, Calabashes, Poe, Taro, &c., while each individual provided himself with the solace of a staff of sugar cane, which shortens with the distance, for the pedestrian, when tired and thirsty, sits down and bites an inch or two off the end of his staff."

David delighted in painting a picture of people met on his visits. He was never the detached scientific traveller who despised the natives. His balanced outlook in life held a place for his fellows wherever and however they lived. The place he passed the night provided a picture to paint with his verbal brush.

"Four old women were inmates of the same dwelling, one of whom, eighty years of age, with hair white as snow, was engaged in feeding two favourite cats with fish. My little terrier disputed the fare with them, to no small annoyance of their mistress. A well-looking young female amused me with singing, while she engaged in cooking a dog over heated stones."

The following morning the old lady was stuffing food into a dog instead of the cats. David was informed that this force-feeding was to fatten the dog for future cooking. She called out to a black pig, using "words which would seem to set orthography at defiance." On answering the call, the poor porker was despatched to provide a picnic for the party. Thus supplied, they set off for the summit of Kilauea. Soon above the tree line David described the panorama.

"Here I beheld one of the grandest scenes imaginable; Mouna Roa reared its bold front, covered with snow, far above the region of verdure, while Mouna Kuah was similarly clothed, to the timber region on the South side, while the summit was cleared of snow that had fallen on the nights of the 12th and the two previous days.

The district of Hilo, Byron's Bay, which I had quitted the previous day, presented from its great moisture, a truly lovely appearance, contrasting in a striking manner with the country where I then stood, and which extended to the sea, whose surface bore evident signs of having been repeatedly ravaged by volcanic fires."

Inspirational as was that early morning scene, it paled before end of the day. It riveted David Douglas. He was hypnotised by this hell of boiling fire. "The noise was dreadful beyond description."

"As the sun sunk beyond the western flank of Mouna Roa, the splendour of the scene increased; but when the full moon rose in a cloudless sky, and shed her fiery brightness on the fiery lake, roaring and boiling in awful majesty, the spectacle became so commanding, that I lost a fine night for astronomical observations, by gazing at the volcano."

Mesmerised by this awful majesty, David found it hard to leave. They camped on the edge of the crater. Unlike others, he sat gazing into the fiery furnace. Once again his soul was stirred.

"How insignificant are the operations of man's hands, taken at their vastest extent, when compared with the magnitude of the works of God".

Douglas descended from the mountain to spend the Sabbath in the native village of Kapupala. It was a Christian community resembling the Sunday's of his youth in Scone. David's devotions were private as he had not their language. However, this day of worship impressed him.

"Honori, my guide, interpreter, purveyor, and, I may say, friend (for in ever department of his omnifarious capacity he is a good sort of fellow), preached today, Sunday the 26th, in his own language, to an assembly of both sexes, old and young, nearly two hundred in number, both morning and evening.....

I visited the school in the interval, when Honori had retired to compose his second sermon, and found the chief, who appears a good man, though far from an apt scholar; they were reading the second chapter of the Epistle to the Galatians, and proceeded to the third, reading verse and verse, all round.....

It is most gratifying to see, far beyond the pale of what is called civilisation,this proper sanctification of the Lord's Day, not only consisting of a cessation from the ordinary duties, but in reading and reflecting upon the purifying and consolatory doctrines of Christianity."

Two days later they set off again, a total party of thirteen. Two guides had been engaged from the village. The elder came highly recommended by the chief. He was a professional bird catcher, providing the feathers for the ceremonial cloaks. As usual they did not travel light but burdened by the mass of food. Some avoided having much of the botanist's burdens. One caused David to recall his Burns.

"Among my attendants was one singular-looking personage, a stripling, who carried a small packed of instruments, and trotted away, arrayed in 'a Cutty-Sark' of most 'scanty longitude', the upper portion of which had once been of white, and the lower of red flannel."

As usual the column struggled uphill straggling behind their leader. As before he thirsted because the person with the provisions was last. David's immediate companion was the bird catcher, Calipio by name. That night they slept below the stars, many stars. "Never, even under a tropical sky, did I behold so many stars."

"Wednesday, January the 29th - the morning rose bright and clear, but cold from the influence of a keen mountain breeze. As the man who carried the provisions was still missing, the preparation of breakfast occupied by little time, so that, accompanied by the bird catcher and Cutty-Sark, I started to half-past six for the summit of the mountain."

The lava proved "terrible beyond description." No doubt missing their breakfast, his helpers were disheartened by cold and fatigue. It was a problem to get them to proceed. When David was ahead they sat down and became deaf to his call. Mauna Loa was inactive but no less a challenge for all that. The broken ridges were covered with snow, here was no hot hell of Kilauea.

They descended to the tree line still unable to find the followers. With plenty of fuel they kindled a fine fire. The light and warmth affected David.

"I found myself instantly seized with a violent pain and inflammation in my eyes, which had been rather painful on the mountain, from the effect of the sun's rays on the snow; a slight discharge of blood from both eyes followed, which gave me some relief."

Those eyes, first found wanting in the Blue Mountains, which required a large print Bible from Glasgow, were now damaged beyond redemption. They were to be less and less effective.

Totally exhausted and famished, that night David dreamt "of gurgling cascades, overhung with sparking rainbows, of which the dew spray moistened my whole body." Hunger and hallucinations were banished when Honori was found making breakfast. Iced water helped the thirst. "A few drops of opium in the eyes afforded instant relief."

David Douglas descended that mountain with a sense of satisfaction and relief. Like the Gaelic poet of Ben Dobhrain, he writes a last farewell to the mountain.

"Gratified though one may be at witnessing the wonderful works of God in such a place as the summit of this mountain presents, still it is with thankfulness that again we approach a climate more congenial to our natures, and welcome the habitations of our fellow men, where we are refreshed with the scent of vegetation, and soothed by the melody of birds."

Almost thirty-five years old, prematurely aged, progressively becoming blinder, David Douglas was now down the hill of life. He almost echoes the Drummond poet.

"Its good to see great mountains, but its better to live on the plain. " The plain of Perthshire might have been the place of his remaining years if his ship had appeared. No sail was to come to take him home to Scotland, Stormont, and Scone.

Spring passed and summer came as David Douglas continued in the Sandwich Islands. He was the Scientific Traveller to the last. He walked the valleys and lower slopes of this lotus land. Richard Charlton, the British Consul at Honolulu wrote a letter to London on the 6th August 1834.

"My dear Sir, - It has devolved on me to inform you of the melancholy death of our friend, poor Douglas. On his arrival at this island, he took the first opportunity of visiting Hawaii, where he remained for some time, with great satisfaction to himself, and usefulness to the public. After his return to this island, he suffered much from rheumatism; but on the 3rd ultimo, finding himself quite recovered, he re-embarked for Hawaii. On the 19th ult., I received the accompanying letter from Messers Diell and Goodrich, two gentleman belonging to the Mission."

The American missionaries, who had been such good friends to David Douglas in those last weeks of his life wrote to "Richard Charlton Esq., His Brittanic Majesty's Consul at the Sandwich Islands," on the 15th July 1834 from Hilo.

"Dear Sir, - Our hearts almost fail us when we undertake to perform the melancholy duty which devolves upon us, to communicate the painful intelligence of the death of our friend Mr. Douglas, and such particulars as we have been able to gather respecting this distressing providence."

A native had arrived at their door at eight o'clock in the morning of the previous day. His face betrayed the bad news before he spoke.

"He communicated the dreadful intelligence, that the body had been found on the mountains, in a pit excavated for the purpose of taking wild cattle, and he was supposed to have been killed by a bullock which was in the pit."

The native had brought the body in a canoe. Nothing had prepared them for the sight of that corpse in the canoe. They washed it and found it in a shocking state, broken and bruised. Their personal agony cries out.

"Can it be he? can it be he? we each exclaimed. Can it be the man with whom we parted but a few days before, and who was borne up with so high spirits and expectations and whom, but an hour previously, we were fondly anticipating to welcome to our little circle."

On the way to the shore, the missionaries further questioned the native. He had only been employed to bring the body along the coast to Hilo. His informants were the natives who bore it to him. His tale was retold in the letter.

"Mr. D. left Rohala Point last week, in company with a foreigner (an Englishman) as a guide, and proceeded to cross Mouna Roa on the North side - tha on the 12th he dismissed the guide, who cautioned him on parting, to be very careful lest he should fall into the pits....Soon after Mr. D. had dismissed his guide, he went back a short distance to get some bundle which he had forgotten, and as he was retracing his steps, at some fatal moment he tumbled into one of the pits in which a bullock had previously fallen - that he had there been found by the natives."

They went for this mysterious guide, who returned and shot the bullock, retrieved the body and sent it on its way. He would follow with the botanist's effects and the wee dog.

The missionaries decided to bury the body at once. However, their helper, a non-native who had been in the cattle business, cast doubts on the wounds and the story. They too had doubts.

Mr. Diell had sailed with Douglas in the boat from Honolulu. Not only had he seen him landed on Hawaii, but he had lent him his servant, John. The coloured man was missing. Where was he? How had Douglas fallen into a trap containing a live animal? They decided to try to preserve the remains and send them to Honolulu. Two non-natives were sent to view the scene. The missing guide was believed to be an Englishman, a convict from Botany Bay. At three o'clock in the afternoon, the latter arrived. His name was Edward Gurney and he told them the full story.

Douglas had called at his house and asked for directions. After breakfast Ned had gone with him to the path and warned him of the traps about two and a half miles ahead. The coloured man, presumably with a native guide, had been sent on ahead. Ned told the same tale as the natives regarding retrieving the body. With his help the missionaries drew diagrams of the fatal spot.

A Mr. Martin bore their letter and Douglas's effects plus Billy, the faithful friend who had, like Greyfriars Bobby, stayed by his master.

The Consul had the remains examined by two doctors. They concurred that the injuries were consistent with the story. He arranged the funeral.

"The next day, I had his remains deposited in their last resting place; the funeral was attended by Captain Seymour and several of the officers of His Majesty's Ship Challenger, and the whole of the foreign Residents. I have caused his grave to be built over with brick, and perhaps his friends may send a stone to be placed (with an inscription) on it.

Twenty two years were to pass before a visitor to Honolulu heard the story and ordered a monument in California. The Reverend Julius L. Brenchley's marble tombstone was engraved in Latin.

A Californian newspaper of 1856 recorded the event. It tells that David Douglas had been buried among the ordinary natives and his grave lost. The distinction the stone would give was long overdue.

On the centenary of his death, the Hilo Burns Club marked the place of his passing by a cairn and planted a grove of Douglas Fir. On the National Geographic Society's map of the State of Hawaii it is marked as Dr. D. Douglas Historic Monument. The native word Kaluakauka is included, meaning 'the Doctor's Pit'.

The American missionaries at Hilo concluded their letter to the British Consul thus. "It is no common death which thus call forth our tears and sympathies: it presents a most affecting comment on the truth, that in the midst of life we are in death"

For years, David Douglas had danced with death on land and rivers. Almost on his way home to Scotland, he had explored a few furlongs too far. Like the writer of the famous Jacobite Ballad, he would take the low road (of the spirit) to return to Scotland.

CHAPTER TEN

Ecotopia, Scotland, and Scone

"The Forests of America, however slighted by man, must have been a great delight to God: for they were the best he ever planted. The whole continent was a garden".

David Douglas had decided to write a book after his initial expedition to Ectopia. This might have been its opening sentence. It comes instead from the works of another Scot who gave his longer life to travelling and writing on the same area. John Muir from Dunbar was born in 1838, four years after David's death. At San Francisco, he entered Ecotopia a tramp on the 27th March 1868. From there he tramped inland to Yosemite Valley, high in the Sierra Nevada. There, among the Giant Redwoods, he devoted his life to saving as much of the Pacific Maritime Forest as possible from unregulated logging.

During 1903, President Theodore Roosevelt came to meet him at Yosemite. They slept below the stars. Talks round camp fires led to over a million acres of forest being conserved. John Muir, the Father of Conservation in America, saved so much of that ecological treasure David Douglas delighted to describe.

Despite the great area designated for preservation, conflict continues on the Coast. Conservationists still oppose certain areas of clearance by logging. Douglas County in Oregon is one such place. David is part of the local folk lore in this part of the United States which claims to be the timber capital of the world. Ships sail from here laden with lumber. Some reach the continent of Europe, some sail to Scotland., the United Kingdom still imports nearly ninety percent of its always increasing requirements of timber. Scotland plays a major role in reducing the deficit using mainly the trees Douglas and his successors introduced from Western North America.

People from the Pacific Coast today fly into Scotland, many are in search of a land left by their ancestors. They are usually not disappointed in their ethnic quest. Seeing the trees they left behind is surprising but a matter of great interest. The fact that it is such a Scottish story adds to the interest.

Tall trees attract attention, especially when they rise directly from fertile flat land. Policy woodlands round laird's houses are mainly on valley bottoms. Most have a matrix of broadleaved trees, green in summer, gold in autumn, but bare in winter. Then particularly, the great conifers, often standing proud as individuals, make their major contribution to the rural scene. They are the spires in a townscape.

The farmland, improved to great productivity since the eighteenth century;

the gardens and arboreta reflecting plants native and naturalised; the mansion house, often an ancient castle redesigned to Enlightenment standards; the contents of such houses are priceless; taken together all facets form great centres of heritage. Scone, still the centre of a modern managed estate, is one of the greatest.

The gardens and arboreta are a tribute to successful partnerships between laird and gardeners since the days of David Douglas. They initially used his plants outside the London and Glasgow specialist gardens, where they were first grown. The first specimens of trees, now common, were expensive to purchase and hard to obtain. Scotland soon required its own source of seed. Perthshire provided the man to get the matter moving, Lord Glenalmond. He brought about the formation of the Oregon Association. Perthshire provided their collector, John Jeffrey. Like David Douglas, his travels of 1851 were tough. Like Douglas, he sent seed home but never returned. His disappearance and death remains a mystery.

The new trees in time moved out of the arboreta to enrich the woods of the estates. They joined the native species and the many obtained from Europe. The success of those introduced species goes to the lairds of last century and their foresters. One such partnership worthy of mention was that of Sir John Stirling Maxwell and his Head Forester, Simon Cameron. The former initiated a pioneer venture on high land round Loch Ossian on the Perthshire Inverness border north of Rannoch. Species and treatments were carried out on this demanding experimental area. The results laid the foundations of modern Scottish forestry on the uplands. Simon Cameron's son, Alister, in Strathyre during the years 1934 - 67 produced the perfect forest in variety and design. His garden complimented his professional work.

However, successful the gardens and forests where the plants introduced by David Douglas are grown, Scone Parish is that shrine where his memory is kept alive. by the church which was moved to the village of New Scone, is that mighty monument so lovingly refurbished by a proud people. Its principal panel reads as follows -

1847

Erected by the lovers of botany in Europe

in memory of

DAVID DOUGLAS

a native of this parish
who from an ardent love of science and
a desire to promote the improvement in botany,
visited the unexplored regions on the banks
of the Columbia River and southward of California.
whence he transmitted a great variety of the seeds
of valuable trees and flowering plants
adapted to the climate of Great Britain,
and who, after devoting ten years of the prime of life
in adding to the arboretum and flora of Europe,
suffered an accidental and lamented death
in one of the Sandwich Islands,
on the 13th July 1834, in the 35th year of his age.
Endowed with an acute and vigorous mind,
which he improved by diligent study,
this eminent botanist
uniformly exemplified in his conduct
those Christian virtues which invested his character
with a higher and more imperishable distinction
than he justly acquired
by his well-earned reputation for scientific knowledge.
A dutiful son, a kind and affectionate brother,
a sincere friend, he secured by the rectitude
of his moral and religious principles,
not less than by the benevolence of his disposition,
the esteemed regard for all who knew his worth.

The other panel reads -

The following are a few of the numerous
trees, shrubs
and
ornamental plants
introduced by
DOUGLAS

Trees

Acer circinatum	Pinus lambertiana
------- macrophyllum	-------- ponderosa
Amelanchier florida	-------- nobilis
Arbutus procera	-------- amabilis
Crataegus douglasii	-------- menziesii

Pinus douglasii

Shrubs

Berberis acquifolium	Ribes sanguineum
-------------- glumacea	-------- speciosum
Garrya elliptica	Rubus spectabilis

Gaultheria shallon

Annuals, Biennials, and Perenials

Clarkia Pulchella	Gillia tricolor
Clintonia elegans	Nemophilia insiginis
Collinsia grandiflora	Ipomopsis elegans

Lupinus poryphyllus
Eachscholtzia californica
Douglasia nivalis
&c. &c.

Those are a sample of over two hundred plants acknowledged to be introduced to Britain by David Douglas. The most extensive list published to date is contained in Appendix Three of Douglas of the Forests by John Davis, published in 1980 by Harris. The world of botany is indebted to him for this excellent list by botanical and common names, as well as the edited republication of the Journal.

"You will begin to think that I manufacture Pines at my pleasure. " so wrote David Douglas to Professor Hooker at a time when most confers were classified as Pines. The Pinetum at Scone Palace embodies a collection of coniferous trees from over the temperate world. Most are over 150 years, new specimens are being added. This treasury of trees can be visited from Easter to September when both Palace and policy are open to visitors.

Across from the entrance to the Palace is an avenue leading to and through the ancient archway which was the entrance to the Abbey bounds. Through it, still stands the mercat cross of the old burgh of Scone. The Wild Garden runs from here towards the Pinetum proper. Past the graveyard is that special Douglas Fir, Pseudotsuga menziesii, grown from the seed sent from the Columbia River in 1826. Fully in view from the Palace, it has pride of place. This is an arboreal monument to David Douglas and his first employer, the third Earl of Mansfield. Plots of plants lie beyond tended at present by a young lady gardener. They have specimens of Douglas flowers. Plans are in hand to have more for 1999.

Douglas firs are the pride of the Pinetum, many standing over 150 feet high (46 metres). In his paper on "some American Pines" Douglas wrote that "some arrived at a magnitude exceeded by few if any trees in the world.....The actual measurement of the largest was of the following dimensions; entire length 227 feet, 48 feet in circumference 3 feet above the ground." Those trees were countless centuries old when seen. David was correct in his assumption of their place in the league table of height. It is believed they may have reached 400 feet. Tallest Douglas Fir today in the United States is 329 feet, the second tallest tree in the country. Tallest of its kind and tallest tree in the British Isles, is a Douglas Fir north of Scone, at the Hermitage near Dunkeld, standing at 212 feet (64.5 metres). It has an Argyll rival. Douglas Fir is a valuable plantation tree on suitable soil.

The lesser in height but lovely to view, are the silver firs. Much less extensive in Ecotopia, David found them on the Cascade Mountains. Visitors to Scone will find worthy specimens there. Their beauty attracts attention.

The Grand Fir, Abies Grandis, stands at 147 feet (45 metres). Perthshire has many specimens in its policies but must yield to Argyll for the champion. The tallest Grand Fir in the British Isles grows at the head of Loch Fyne, Ardkinglas, at present 206 feet (63 metres), second tallest tree overall below the Douglas Fir. However, Perthshire has the plantation of greatest growth, north of Dunkeld above the Tay.

The Noble Fir, Abies procera, could bear no other name. Sublime in their symmetry, they stand at Scone. How David Douglas would delight in seeing them there, as he did in their natural habitat. It was by far the finest, he walked for three weeks where it was dominant and never ceased to admire it.

"The trees are straight, one hundred and seventy feet high........an inhabitant only of the mountains, seldom seen to arrive at any considerable size lower down the hills than 5000 feet above the level of the sea."

David would have been delighted to find that his native land would have given a happy home to his find and changed that statement. The tallest Noble Fir growing in the British Isles is probably about fifty feet above the sea. At the head of Loch Fyne is to be found a noble specimen of 167 feet (51 metres). Perthshire provides many magnificent examples.

David declares its worth and predicts its potential as a plantation tree. "This if introduced would profitably clothe the bleak barren hilly parts of Scotland, Ireland, Cumberland, besides increasing the beauty of the country." It did find a place in our woods and forest and is still planted for its beauty. However, that prediction of profitability on the barren hills was to be realised by his greatest but least appreciated introduction, Sitka Spruce.

The tallest of its kind and second tallest tree in the British Isles, grows in Perthshire, but has a location not to be revealed to the public. This Sitka Spruce, picea sitchensis, has a height of 202 feet (61 metres). The tallest in the United States is 113 feet higher and their third tallest tree. Where growing naturally, it is the ultimate tree of Ecotopia. Over 1500 miles it clung to the coastline, only going inland up gently rising river valleys such as the Hoh where it is still preserved. The Queen Charlotte Islands off the coast of British Columbia are the great, well tried, seed source for Scotland.

If the public are denied sight of the tallest specimen, they are welcome to see striking specimens at Scone. Those four venerable trees are a diamond within the oldest part of the pinetum, planted post 1850. Even scorners of this super species, sadly they are many, could not fail to be impressed by the character of those fine trees. Standing solid, with circumference around 22 feet and heights of over 140 feet, they dominate their slimmer, equally tall, fellows. They form the principal focus of the pinetum. David Douglas would have been baffled by the apparent bias against Sitka Spruce by opinion formers today. He had no doubts about its inherent value.

"The appearance of this species closely resembles P. Douglasii; although neither so large nor so plentiful as that species, it may nevertheless become of equal if not greater importance, as it possesses one great advantage over that one by growing to a very large size on the Northern declivity's of the mountain in apparently poor, thin, damp soils; and even in rocky places, where there is a sufficiency of earth to cover the the horizontal wide-spreading roots, their growth is so far from being regarded that they exceed one hundred feet high and eight feet in circumference. This unquestionably has great claims on our consideration as it would thrive in such places as Britain where even P. Sylvestris finds no shelter. It would become a useful and large tree."

Scottish silviculturalists succeeded in realising David's dreams. It became super Sitka Spruce, the coloniser of Scotland's wet desert, this century. Paper print mills came to give employment, this white timber of long fibre is their preferred. Scottish timber merchants cannot obtain enough of this timber, it flows south to their competitors. The people of Scotland's industrial belt spend Sundays walking through forests of this and other David Douglas's importations. Despite some propaganda in print, there is no evidence to suggest that tourists find them abhorrent.

What of the flowers of the forest found in gardens from castles to cottages? Harvey, the Western North American author writer says of them - "Hardly a garden exists that does not have the clarkia, mariposa lily, California poppy, or some of the lupines, phlox, penstemons, mimulus, or others of his beautiful flowers."

An English admirer wrote - "there is scarcely a spot deserving the name of garden, either in Europe or the United States in which some of the discoveries of Douglas do not form the chief attraction."

Lachlan Buchanan, in Perthshire wrote - "His true memorials are the living, growing, trees and plants which he brought from the New World, and which do so much to brighten our gardens as the seasons come and go. Consider some of them: flowering currants, antirrhinums, phlox, penstemons, mimulus, godetia, lupins, clarkia, Californian Poppy, heuchera, and many others.

First on that list is flowering currant, flourishing in April, an early indicator of the beauty to come. It was said of it, that if David Douglas's first expedition to Ecotopia had produced this alone, the cost would have been justified. Unaware of the provider, gardeners focus on their favourites.

The concept of a municipal garden to educate people on the extent of this horticultural heritage arose in Perth early in the Sixties. The Royal Horticultural Society of Perthshire, the motivator of the Monument over a century before, was the prime mover. At the time, its President, Lord Elphinstone, said that "the directorate feels that it has a moral duty to ensure the perpetuation of the memory of this most intrepid and versatile of explorers." Below Balhousie Castle, on the North Inch of Perth, a site was found. Plants and seeds were procured from many sources in the United Kingdom and the United States. During 1962, the David Douglas Memorial Garden became reality. Lachlan Buchanan wrote that "a living, lasting memorial has at last been created to perpetuate the memory of David Douglas". It was not to be, the noble project was neglected after the old Burgh of Perth was amalgamated into a larger unit of local government.

Scone Parish, which had so magnificently refurbished the great Monument by the old Kirk, decided to move on to a living monument. Scone village, a bonnie place, took top place in Perthshire and came second in Scotland in the Beautiful Scotland in Bloom competition for 1993. Impressed by the community's spirit, the judges suggested that they might move to a memorial garden. One year later, that same President of the David Douglas Society of North America, who had honoured the rededication of the Monument, returned to attend the opening of the David Douglas Memorial Garden. A Society of Friends of the Garden has been formed.

On the 13th May 1997, a meeting is moted in Scone to form the ultimate tribute to their "lad o' pairts", a David Douglas Society. It is proposed to call it "The David Douglas Society."

"The object of the Society will be to perpetuate the name of the explorer and botanist David Douglas throughout the world. This will be done by arranging public meetings, lectures, film shows, exhibitions, by educating the public, both young and old, on the achievements of David Douglas."

Scone, which has done so much since that grey October day in 1988, will move forward to meet those aims with support from all who honour the memory of that brave man. The two hundredth anniversary of his humble birth during 1999 will not pass unnoticed.

SELECT BIBLIOGRAPHY

Journal kept by David Douglas during his Travels in North America 1823-1827. Wesley & Son. London. 1914

This is the "bible" printed in first form. Its principal content is the original journal of David Douglas as written. There is also a concise account of his travels by him. This contains interesting little items of information not mentioned in the main account. Douglas's papers on North American Oaks and Pines (conifers) are also reproduced. His long account to his brother of his explorations in Hawaii is included and also the correspondence at the time of his death.

All praise should be given to those who made this archive available to the world and libraries like the present Bell Library in Perth, who make it available so readily. This treasure was the main source of this book.

The first book written on David Douglas, Douglas of the Fir, by A. G. Harvey, published by Harvard University Press. 1947, remains the most comprehensive yet in North America.

There have been two semi-fictional works. It would have been surprising that such a subject had not attracted writers in this genre. Traveller in a Vanished Landscape, by William Morwood, was published by Gentry Books, London. 1973. Children of North America were given a gem in Plant Detective: David Douglas, by Bob and Jan Young, published by Julian Messner New York, 1966.

John Davis undertook the task of providing an edited edition of David Douglas's Journal on the period of his first journey to the West Coast of North America, from his arrival there on April 8th 1825 to his arrival at Hudson Bay on the 28th August 1827. Entitled Douglas of the Forests, it was published by Paul Harris, 1980. I found it invaluable on my journeys through Oregon, Washington and British Columbia.